Tasks Of Problem Solving: Adolescent

MW00415426

by Linda Bowers, Rosemary Huisingh and Carolyn LoGiudice

Skills	Ages
■ problem solving	■ 12-17
■ language	**Grades**
■ listening	■ 7-12
■ critical thinking	

Evidence-Based Practice

According to the Adolescent Medicine (2006), some common signs indicating a progression from more simple to more complex cognitive development include:

■ *Early adolescence* - during early adolescence, the use of more complex thinking is focused on personal decision making in school and home environments (e.g., begins to demonstrate use of formal logical operations in schoolwork).

■ *Middle adolescence* - expands to include more philosophical and futuristic concerns (e.g., questions and analyzes more extensively).

■ *Late adolescence* - complex thinking processes are used to focus on less self-centered concepts as well as personal decision making (e.g., had increased thoughts about more global concepts such as justice, history, politics, and patriotism).

Jean Piaget talks about "developmental stages" and times when children are acquiring new ways of mentally representing information. In the final stage of cognitive development, called the *formal operational state* (age 12 years to adulthood), children begin to develop a more theoretical view of the world. Thoughts become more abstract, incorporating the principles of formal logic. This stage is achieved by most children, although failure to do so has been associated with lower intelligence.

According to the school Improvement Research Series (2006), teaching students to become critical thinkers is an essential education goal.

■ Direct teaching of critical thinking enhances students' critical thinking skills and application.

■ Students have the ability to improve their thinking skills if they are taught how to think critically.

The information in this book incorporates the above principles and is also based on expert professional practice.

LinguiSystems

LinguiSystems, Inc.
3100 4th Avenue
East Moline, IL 61244
800-776-4332

FAX: 800-577-4555
Email: service@linguisystems.com
Web: linguisystems.com

Printed in the U.S.A.

ISBN 978-0-7606-0744-2

About the Authors

■ **Linda Bowers**, M.A., SLP, is a co-founder and co-owner of LinguiSystems. She is a speech-language pathologist with wide experience serving language-disordered students of all ages. Linda has a keen professional interest in the critical thinking and language abilities of children and adults.

■ **Rosemary Huisingh**, M.A., SLP, is also a co-founder and co-owner of LinguiSystems. As a speech-language pathologist, she has successfully served the communication needs of school-aged children for many years. Rosemary is particularly interested in childhood language, vocabulary and thinking skills.

■ **Carolyn LoGiudice**, M.A., CCC-SLP, coordinates product acquisitions at LinguiSystems and also develops and edits products. Carolyn has broad experience as an SLP serving school-aged children and is especially interested in the pragmatics and thinking skills of children and adolescents.

Linda, Rosemary and Carolyn are the authors of the *Test Of Problem Solving 2 – Adolescent*. They are also co-authors of the following:

- *The Listening Comprehension Test 2*
- *The WORD Test 2 – Elementary*
- *The WORD Test 2 – Adolescent*
- *Story Comprehension To Go*
- *Spotlight on Reading & Listening Comprehension*
- *No-Glamour Language & Reasoning*
- *No-Glamour Language & Reasoning Cards*
- *No-Glamour Language & Reasoning Interactive Software*

Illustrations by Margaret Warner
Cover design & page layout by Lisa Parker
Photographs from *istockphoto.com* © 2006 iStock International, Inc.

Table of Contents

Introduction

We love this quote because it reminds us of who we *used* to be as thinkers. We'd say things like "I'm so tired of thinking, my brain hurts" or "Wake me up when the thinking part is over." Fortunately, it's been years since we awakened and smelled the delicious aroma of freshly-brewed thinking . . . aggressive, pungent and strong with a confusing mix of other unidentified sensations.

For nearly 30 years we've been entrenched in the research on thinking, cognition and problem solving, and we're still as enthusiastic as ever about making every therapy session and every classroom a hotbed of teaching thinking. One of our grandchildren recently completed kindergarten with a teacher so amazing in her ability to draw out students' thoughts that this author just had to spend time in her classroom. To this author's surprise, this gifted teacher was using higher-order questioning, meant for children much older, with most of the students. If a student made the observation that a caterpillar should be able to walk more quickly because of all of its legs, she asked, "Why do you think so?" or "What do you see about its body that might give you a clue that it can't?" Obviously this teacher never felt restricted by the language or vocabulary that she used and never underestimated how youngsters could think. Even the lowest-functioning student in that kindergarten class could answer questions above the third level of Bloom's Taxonomy, Application.

Tasks Of Problem Solving – Adolescent is a rich compendium of situations in which adolescents find themselves. Each unit works on a specific skill and incorporates other thinking skills as well. These are the units:

- Sequencing
- Asking and Answering Questions
- Comparing and Contrasting
- Identifying Problems
- Detecting Key Information
- Making Inferences

- Expressing Consequences
- Determining Solutions
- Justifying Opinions
- Interpreting Perspectives
- Transferring Insights
- Integrating Thinking Skills

Within these units, you'll see the other skills embedded in associated tasks.

Discovery consists of looking at the same thing as everyone else and thinking something different.
Albert Szent-Gyorgyi, biochemist

The work of Richard Paul, 2004, shows 35 higher-order thinking skills that are divided into three areas:

- affective strategies
- cognitive strategies – macroabilities
- cognitive strategies – microskills

These areas and their strategies are listed on pages 6-8.

■ Affective Strategies

thinking independently
having one's own thoughts

developing insights into egocentricity or sociocentricity
understanding that one's thoughts may be self-motivated or motivated by societal influences

exercising fairmindedness
seeing all sides of issues and understanding them fully before judging

exploring thoughts underlying feelings and feelings underlying thoughts
separating emotion from fact and vice versa

developing intellectual humility and suspending judgment
waiting to form an opinion until one knows all the facts

developing intellectual courage
having the strength to put off judgment in the face of pressure from others

developing intellectual good faith or integrity
the courage and ability to be honest and faithful in the pursuit of truthfulness

developing intellectual perseverance
continuing to consider and reconsider issues over time to gain insight, despite confusion or frustration

developing confidence in reason
trusting that others will reach logical conclusions if they are free to reason

■ Cognitive Strategies — Macroabilities

refining generalizations and avoiding oversimplifications
drilling down through overstatement and adding relevant detail

comparing analogous situations: transferring insights into new contexts
one's ability to apply what's been learned to a new situation

developing one's perspective: creating or exploring beliefs, arguments or theories
one's ability to compare perspectives with others for validation and truthfulness

clarifying issues, conclusions or beliefs
one's ability to develop and articulate thoughts clearly to others

clarifying and analyzing the meanings of words or phrases
knowing words and phrases that are "loaded" with offensive thinking

developing criteria for evaluation: clarifying values and standards
knowing how to prepare documents to verify beliefs

evaluating the credibility of sources of information
understanding that a written or spoken opinion is not necessarily true

questioning deeply: raising and pursuing root or significant questions
one's ability to drill down questions to core issues

analyzing or evaluating arguments, interpretations, beliefs or theories
knowing how to question deeply

generating or assessing solutions
knowing how to prepare a set of results from which to choose

analyzing or evaluating actions or policies
one's ability to question authority, rules and other issues

reading critically: clarifying or critiquing texts
one's ability to never accept what's read as true until further investigation is done satisfactorily

listening critically: the art of silent dialogue
questioning and discussing internally as one listens

making interdisciplinary connections
understanding that learning a subject crosses subjects

practicing Socratic discussion: clarifying and questioning beliefs, theories or perspectives
asking open-ended questions to further discuss generalizations

reasoning dialogically: comparing perspectives, interpretations or theories
having dialogues with others about issues of thought

reasoning dialectically: evaluating perspectives, interpretations or theories
thinking about issues affected by societal input

Cognitive Strategies — Microskills

comparing and contrasting ideals with actual practice
listing the pros and cons of real-life decisions

thinking precisely about thinking
using critical vocabulary to think

noting significant similarities and differences
recording these for reference as issues take shape

examining or evaluating assumptions
recording assumptions and asking about their relevance

distinguishing relevant from irrelevant facts
sorting through what is and isn't germane

making plausible inferences, predictions or interpretations
one's ability to make only realistic choices, leaving others out

giving reasons and evaluating evidence and alleged facts
separating fact from fiction and providing evidence as support

recognizing contradictions
being able to articulate differences on an issue

exploring implications and consequences
investigating all of the realistic ideas and results of an issue

Paul (2004) summarizes the global concept of *thinking* as:

> the intellectually disciplined process of actively and skillfully conceptualizing, applying, analyzing, synthesizing and/or evaluating information gathered from, or generated by, observation, experience, reflection, reasoning or communication, as a guide to belief and action

The skills listed on pages 6-8, when woven into lessons on a very conscious level, can have tremendous impact on the gains students of all abilities make toward becoming better thinkers. You will find these skills throughout *Tasks Of Problem Solving – Adolescent*.

> *Don't overlook the importance of world-wide thinking. A country that keeps its eye on Tom, Dick and Harry is going to miss Pierre, Hans and Yoshio.* Al Ries, author

In 2002, Arthur Costa, noted researcher in the area of critical thinking, wrote the article *Educating the Global Intellect*. In it he wrote that many societies formerly thought of as underdeveloping nations are showing great signs of applied intellect: *creativity, problem solving and reasoning skills in a climate of entrepreneurship, freedom and collaboration.*

Dr. Costa's early research still applies today. In 1991 he outlined 14 Intelligent Behaviors which were gratefully accepted by teachers around the world. Since then, he has perfected these behaviors into 16 attributes of Habits of Mind, which are listed on pages 9 and 10.

■ Habits of Mind

1 persisting – sticking to a task or thought until it is completed . . . and going at it again

2 managing impulsivity – thinking before acting . . . and thinking again

3 listening to others – listening with understanding and empathy by seeing and acknowledging the highest forms of communication, cues

4 thinking flexibly – the capacity to change one's mind as one receives additional data

5 thinking about our thinking – the ability to know what we know and recognize what we don't know

6 striving for accuracy and precision – taking time to check over one's product to achieve excellence

7 questioning and posing problems – the ability to fill in the gaps between what is known and not known

8 applying past knowledge to new situations – learning from experience

9 thinking and communicating with clarity and precision – refining language so that communication is less ambiguous

10 gathering data through all senses – developing sensory sensitivity to information we receive through our five senses

11 creating, imagining and innovating – developing the capacity to generate something novel, original, clever or ingenious

12 responding with wonderment and awe – having a passion for what one does

13 taking responsible risks – accepting confusion, uncertainty and the high risk of failure as part of normal existence

14 finding humor – using laughter to liberate and provoke creativity

15 thinking interdependently – realizing that the sum of the parts is greater than a piece

16 learning continuously – never reaching the end of the learning curve

You will note some overlap between Paul's and Costa's work because most researchers agree about what constitutes higher-order thinking. You'll find this overlap in this manual also.

Intuition will tell the thinking mind where to look next. Jonas Salk, microbiologist

Jean Piaget is known largely as a researcher in the area of early childhood development. He spent considerable time, however, studying the cognitive development of 7 to 12 year olds, and beyond. He divided his studies into two age groups: the group for 7 to 11 year olds is named the *Concrete Operational Stage* and the group for 11 year olds and up is named the *Formal Operational Stage*.

The Concrete Operational Stage is characterized by the use of more complex thinking. Children become focused on personal decision making in school and at home by questioning authority, using logical approaches to understand schoolwork and communicating their own thoughts on issues and concerns. During this stage, students begin to analyze their thoughts and behaviors more closely and begin to think about their individual identities.

The Formal Operational Stage continues the growth of complex thought by focusing on future issues and goals. Students begin to make plans and to think long-term. They use systematic thinking with regard to their relationships with others and have more interest in global issues such as politics, justice, history and patriotism. At this stage you'll see high school debate teams take on serious issues, thus demonstrating that our youth are emerging into adult society.

If I look confused, it's because I'm thinking. Samuel Goldwyn, producer

Adolescents with language disorders show distinct behaviors that reflect their confusion about language use, including:

- failure to understand or pay attention to rules of social language

- difficulty using different language for different listeners or social situations

- incorrect grammar, usually with regard to future tense, conjunctions, compound sentences and modifiers

- poor or limited vocabulary

- difficulty asking for further information to help comprehension

- tendency to ask questions that are too general to gain helpful information

- tendency to agree rather than voice a different opinion

- difficulty interpreting indirect requests and ambiguous statements

- class clown behavior to distract from language difficulties

- excessive forgetfulness

- withdrawal or exclusion from peer group activities

- difficulty with word finding, abstract language, instructions, multiple meaning words, sequencing, organizing and expressing thoughts

Tasks Of Problem Solving – Adolescent will allow you to focus on your students as whole or complete language users because teaching language in the context of higher-order thinking treats youth as thinking, caring people. The therapy you provide with this manual will help your students develop language that adequately reflects their improved thinking skills.

We appreciate all you do,

Linda, Rosemary and Carolyn

Sequencing

A student with effective sequencing skills can organize both objects and ideas quickly and logically. Such an arrangement might be sequenced in increasing or decreasing order according to these and other dimensions:

- numerical order
- alphabetical order
- size
- weight
- height
- length

- density
- distance
- amount
- steps to follow
- intensity
- time or date

- pitch
- frequency of occurrence
- importance
- value
- usefulness
- probability

Many sequences are predictable because they have one obvious order, such as putting socks on before shoes or nesting boxes according to size. Other sequences could follow several logical patterns, such as getting ready for school or studying for a test. More complex sequencing involves evaluating events or ideas according to importance or some other abstract concept, such as prioritizing which patients in an emergency room need what treatment in what order.

Many academic tasks involve sequencing, such as solving math problems, understanding the causes and consequences of historic events or conducting scientific experiments. We can teach students to understand the value of sequencing by posing questions such as these throughout class lessons:

- What happened first/next/last?
- Why did each thing happen?
- What will each character do next? Why?
- What was the most important problem in the story? Why?
- What do we need to know before we can make our chart?
- What is the last thing you should do before you turn in your test?
- What is the first thing you should do after an earthquake?
- How does a bill become a national law in the U.S.?
- When does a disease become an epidemic?

Teach your students to value sequencing their ideas and activities as an effective way to organize themselves and the ways they want to spend their time and energy. Sequencing their assignments gives them more control over their learning and their productivity. Prioritizing their personal values helps them make good choices in their behavior and their relationships with others. People who spontaneously sequence priorities and tasks fluently and purposefully are better able to control their everyday lives and to respond to emergency situations, such as a natural disaster, than those who only sequence things when instructed to do so.

■ Vocabulary

It is important to understand each of these words in order to think and talk about sequencing.

chronological   arranged in order by time

classify   to organize things into groups

explain   to describe how or why something works or is true

identify   to point out or recognize something

justify   to explain why you made a decision, took an action or formed an opinion

logical   sensible

modify   to change a plan, idea or solution

opinion   what you believe or feel about an issue

organize   to arrange things thoughtfully and logically

original   novel, creative, not copied or imitated

plan (n)   sequenced steps to follow to achieve a goal

possibility   something that could happen or could be accomplished

predict   to guess what will happen or the consequence of an action

prioritize   to sequence things according to their importance or need for immediate attention

reason (n)   why something happened, a cause

sequence (v)   to arrange things in a logical order

similarities   ways things or ideas are alike

■ Choose words from the box to complete these sentences correctly. Use each word only once.

chronological	logical	opinion	original	reason
justify	modify	organize	plan	sequence

1 Dates in a timeline are arranged in _____ order.

2 Tell me one _____ it is illegal to drive without a license.

3 Keesha earns money by designing _____ clothing.

4 What is your _____ about having homework over a weekend?

5 Is it _____ to care about the way you look to others?

6 We have to _____ our schedule because a severe storm is coming.

7 In what _____ will you do your assignments tonight?

8 Let's make a _____ for getting together after the game.

9 Connor tried to _____ why he hadn't finished his report.

10 How do you _____ all the things in your closet?

■ Tell how the words in each pair are associated.

1 predict – possibility
2 sequence – prioritize
3 classify – organize
4 reason – justify

■ Sequencing things in the right order is important for many everyday tasks. Write numbers in the blanks to sequence each list in the correct order.

1 Sequence these steps to make a grilled cheese sandwich.

Photo courtesy of istockphoto.com © johanna goodyear

____ **a** Add the top slice of bread.
____ **b** Put the cheese slices onto the bread in the pan.
____ **c** Put one bread slice in a heated frying pan, butter side down.
____ **d** Butter one side of each slice.
____ **e** When the other side of the sandwich has browned, remove the sandwich from the pan.
____ **f** Turn the whole sandwich over when the first slice has browned.
____ **g** Take out two slices of bread and some cheese slices.

2 Sequence these names in the order they would appear in a telephone directory.

____ **a** Gonzales
____ **b** Goethals
____ **c** Martindale
____ **d** Ferguson
____ **e** Thornhill
____ **f** Gripp

3 Sequence these street names in the order they would appear in a map index.

____ **a** Maple Avenue
____ **b** Lopez Street
____ **c** Hudson Lake Street
____ **d** Madison Avenue
____ **e** Mercer Street
____ **f** Grundy Boulevard

4 Sequence these TV shows in chronological order.

____ **a** The Mobsters   Thursday, 9/8, 8:00 p.m.
____ **b** Inside Outside   Monday, 9/5, 7:30 p.m.
____ **c** La Vida   Friday, 9/9, 9:00 p.m.
____ **d** World News   Monday, 9/5, 6:00 p.m.
____ **e** Trader Tom   Thursday, 9/8, 10:00 p.m.
____ **f** Science Rocks   Wednesday, 9/7, 8:30 p.m.
____ **g** Name Your Price   Tuesday, 9/6, 7:00 p.m.
____ **h** Carlos and Rico   Friday, 9/9, 8:30 p.m.

■ Listen to each set of directions. Remember how many steps are in each set. Then restate the directions in the correct order.

1 Making microwave popcorn

[1] Get a bag of microwave popcorn.
[2] Put it in the microwave with the correct side down.
[3] Heat the popcorn on high for about three minutes.
[4] When the popping slows down, take the bag out of the microwave.
[5] Open the bag carefully and pour the popcorn into a bowl.

Photo courtesy of istockphoto.com © Samantha Grandy

2 Hosting a party

[1] Decide the time and date to have the party.
[2] Invite your guests.
[3] Plan what food and drinks you will serve.
[4] Shop for the food and drinks.
[5] Chill the drinks you will serve cold.
[6] Set the food out for your guests.

3 Getting a job

[1] Find out what jobs are available.
[2] Decide which jobs suit your experience, skills and time.
[3] Apply for the jobs.
[4] Be interviewed by employers who will consider hiring you.
[5] If you are offered a job, decide if you want to accept it.
[6] Report to work on time and ready to do your best.

4 Treating a cut

[1] Wash the cut with soap and water.
[2] Dry the cut with a clean towel or paper towel.
[3] Apply antiseptic or antibiotic cream to the cut.
[4] Cover the cut with a clean bandage.
[5] Keep the cut dry and clean.

■ Write numbers in the blanks to sequence each set of events in chronological order.

1 ____ **a** Astronauts landed on the moon.
____ **b** The airplane was invented.
____ **c** The hot-air balloon was invented.

2 ____ **a** Families used candles for light at home.
____ **b** Families used electricity for light at home.
____ **c** Families used gas for light at home.

3 ____ **a** Thomas Jefferson was the U.S. President.
____ **b** George Washington was the U.S. President.
____ **c** Abraham Lincoln was the U.S. President.

Photo courtesy of istockphoto.com © Jim Parkin

4 ____ **a** Pyramids were built in Egypt.
____ **b** The wheel was invented.
____ **c** The Panama Canal was built.

5 ____ **a** Texas became a state.
____ **b** Hawaii became a state.
____ **c** North Carolina became a state.

6 ____ **a** People sent email messages.
____ **b** People sent telegrams.
____ **c** People used telephones to communicate.

7 ____ **a** The first train was invented.
____ **b** People traveled by coach.
____ **c** The riverboat was invented.

8 ____ **a** The Golden Gate Bridge was constructed in San Francisco.
____ **b** France gave the U.S. the Statue of Liberty.
____ **c** The *Mayflower* landed at Plymouth Rock.

9 ____ **a** Jeans were invented during the Gold Rush.
____ **b** Wrinkle-free fabric for shirts was invented.
____ **c** The button was invented.

10 ____ **a** Fresh orange juice came in cartons.
____ **b** Florida had many orange orchards.
____ **c** Orange juice was squeezed from oranges.

Task 5

■ Write numbers in the blanks to sequence each set of items according to the directions.

1 Sequence these items from the least political power to the most political power.

_____ **a** candidate for governor
_____ **b** governor
_____ **c** mayor
_____ **d** president
_____ **e** senator

2 Sequence these items from the least serious to the most serious health condition.

_____ **a** heart attack
_____ **b** mosquito bite
_____ **c** head cold
_____ **d** broken leg
_____ **e** sinus infection
_____ **f** diabetes type 2

3 Sequence these items from the least expensive to the most expensive.

_____ **a** motorcycle
_____ **b** skateboard
_____ **c** baseball
_____ **d** bicycle
_____ **e** helicopter

Photo courtesy of istockphoto.com © ImagesbyTrista

4 Sequence these U.S. history events in chronological order.

_____ **a** California became a state.
_____ **b** The Revolutionary War began.
_____ **c** The Civil War began.
_____ **d** George Washington was elected President.
_____ **e** The U.S. joined the allies to fight World War II.
_____ **f** Hawaii became a state.
_____ **g** The U.S. fought in the Vietnam conflict.

5 Sequence these car trips from the shortest to the longest distance by miles.

_____ **a** Jacksonville, FL to Miami, FL
_____ **b** Philadelphia, PA to Baltimore, MD
_____ **c** Anchorage, AK to Dallas, TX
_____ **d** San Francisco, CA to Oakland, CA
_____ **e** Chicago, IL to New Orleans, LA

1 Bryce enjoys all kinds of music. He plays the guitar and sings with a local band. This year, Bryce wants to get a part in the school musical.

■ Write numbers in the blanks to sequence these steps in the order in which Bryce will do them.

Photo courtesy of istockphoto.com © Donald Linscott

_____ **a** Do his best at the tryouts.

_____ **b** Find out when and where the tryouts will be held.

_____ **c** Perform in the musical.

_____ **d** Look over the musical to see which part or parts look good for him.

_____ **e** Get information about the parts in the musical.

_____ **f** Practice the part or parts he wants to try out for.

_____ **g** Rehearse with the rest of the cast.

2 Charlene has always loved to cook. She wants to be a chef someday. This year, she entered her recipe for grilled asparagus with ginger sauce in a local competition.

■ Write numbers in the blanks to sequence these steps in the order Charlene did them to prepare for the cooking competition.

Photo courtesy of istockphoto.com © Galina Barskaya

_____ **a** Buy fresh ingredients for the competition.

_____ **b** Practice making the recipe.

_____ **c** Choose the recipe to make for the judges.

_____ **d** Prepare the dish for the judges.

_____ **e** Find out the date, time and rules for the competition.

Pirates once ruled the seas. They attacked ships and made them pay a fee in order to sail. As long as the American colonies were part of England, their ships were covered by the fees England paid pirates. Once the U.S. became independent, pirates freely attacked U.S. ships. They captured sailors and sold them in slave markets.

Soon the U.S., like other countries, paid the pirate fees. In 1801, though, the U.S. refused to pay anymore. The U.S. Marines attacked a pirate fort in Tripoli. They raised the U.S. flag over the fort as a sign of victory. Since then, U.S. forces have made sure that ships can cross the ocean without fear of pirate attacks.

Photo courtesy of istockphoto.com © Vaide Seskauskiene

■ Check the best answer for each question.

1 Which event happened first?

_____ **a** The U.S. Marines raised a flag over the pirate fort.
_____ **b** Pirates attacked U.S. ships.
_____ **c** All countries paid fees to pirates in order to sail ships.

2 Which event happened last?

_____ **a** The U.S. became an independent nation.
_____ **b** England's fees to pirates included fees for ships from American colonies.
_____ **c** The U.S. paid pirate fees in order to sail ships.

3 Which events happened at about the same time?

_____ **a** The U.S. Marines defeated a pirate fort in Tripoli and paid the pirate fees.
_____ **b** The U.S. refused to pay pirate fees and attacked a pirate fort.
_____ **c** Pirates charged countries fees for sailing and the U.S. kept the oceans free of pirate dangers.

John Muir inspired people to take action to protect the environment. His love of nature and his writing talent left a legacy we benefit from today.

Photo courtesy of istockphoto.com © Henryk Lippert

John was born in 1838 in Scotland in a small coastal village. In 1849, his family moved to Wisconsin. They lived on a farm and worked hard. When John had time, he roamed the fields and woods nearby. John observed and loved nature. He also invented things, including a device to tip him out of bed.

After three years of college, Muir traveled on his own. He did odd jobs along the way. Over the years, he traveled more and more. He walked from Indianapolis to the Gulf of Mexico. He sailed from there to San Francisco, which he made his home.

In 1868, Muir herded sheep in the high country of the Sierra Nevada and Yosemite. He called the area "the most divinely beautiful of all the mountain chains I have ever seen." Muir wrote articles about this area that encouraged others to witness its beauty. Though he saw scenic places in many other countries, Muir loved the Sierra Nevada best. His many books and articles urged people to stop sheep and cattle from destroying the area. In 1890 the U.S. created Yosemite National Park in part due to Muir's efforts. Muir also helped to create other parks, including the Petrified Forest and Grand Canyon. He was known as the "Father of Our National Park System."

■ Check the best answer for each question.

1 Which event happened first?

_____ **a** John Muir walked to the Gulf of Mexico.
_____ **b** John Muir helped to create Yosemite National Park.
_____ **c** John Muir went to college.

2 Which event happened last?

_____ **a** John Muir was called the "Father of Our National Park System."
_____ **b** John Muir considered San Francisco his home.
_____ **c** John Muir was a sheepherder in Yosemite.

3 Which things happened at the same time?

_____ **a** John Muir stayed in the Sierra Nevada and wrote articles about it.
_____ **b** John Muir was an inventor and lived on a farm.
_____ **c** John Muir went to college and worked in the Sierra Nevada.
_____ **d** both a and b

Ceres, the goddess of plants and harvests, and Jupiter, chief god of justice, had a lovely daughter. Her name was Proserpina. Ceres was close to her daughter. They enjoyed being together and gathering flowers. They wore colorful clothing and nurtured crops and plants.

Photo courtesy of istockphoto.com © malcolm romain

Pluto, god of the underworld, fell in love with Proserpina at first sight. He wanted her as his bride. She would brighten his drab land. He knew she wouldn't marry him of her own free will, so he kidnapped her.

Ceres was heartbroken. She tore the colorful ribbons from her hair. She wore only dark, drab clothing as she searched for her daughter. Without care from Ceres, all plants withered and earth looked dull and drab. Jupiter ordered Pluto to release Proserpina. Pluto agreed, but only if she would eat a pomegranate before she left. She ate just a few seeds to please him. Then she rushed home to her parents. Pluto smiled as she left him.

Ceres and Jupiter were thrilled to have their daughter back. Soon, though, they learned that she had eaten four pomegranate seeds before she left Pluto. "You ate four seeds from his pomegranate," Jupiter told her. "Those seeds are a symbol of faithfulness in marriage. Now you must go back to Pluto for four months every year."

From that day on, nature has followed a sequence of seasons. When Proserpina comes in spring, plants revive and flowers bloom. They flourish over the summer. In the fall, Ceres turns the plants orange and brown, her daughter's favorite colors. While Proserpina is with Pluto, the earth is dormant and cold. The cycle begins again when Proserpina returns to her parents.

■ Check the best answer for each question.

1 Sequence these story events in chronological order.

_____ **a** Proserpina ate some pomegranate seeds.
_____ **b** Pluto kidnapped Proserpina.
_____ **c** Jupiter and Ceres had a daughter named Proserpina.
_____ **d** For the first time, plants withered and earth became dull.
_____ **e** Pluto was lonely and wanted a wife.

2 Which event happened first?

_____ **a** Proserpina ate some seeds from Pluto's pomegranate.
_____ **b** The earth was cold and drab during winter.
_____ **c** Pluto kidnapped Proserpina to be his bride.

■ Each value below is important. Some of these values are probably more important to you than others. Consider each value from your own point of view. Then make a check mark beside your top ten personal values. On the right, list these ten values in order from most important to least important to you.

☐ cooperation

☐ courage

☐ creativity

☐ determination

☐ faith

☐ family

☐ friendship

☐ happiness

☐ honesty

☐ honor

☐ independence

☐ intelligence

☐ love

☐ loyalty

☐ patience

☐ respect

☐ responsibility

☐ simplicity

☐ tolerance

☐ truth

☐ wisdom

☐ world peace

1 _____

2 _____

3 _____

4 _____

5 _____

6 _____

7 _____

8 _____

9 _____

10 _____

Asking and Answering Questions

A critical skill for understanding someone's reasoning is the ability to ask good questions to gather the relevant information you need to comprehend the issues.

We tell our students to "get all the facts" to understand a situation or a problem, but we often forget to check whether each student knows how to ask the right questions to gather relevant information. Some students have trouble asking questions because they lack adequate language skills to formulate and express a question effectively. Other students may be quite able to ask questions, but may not detect the precise information they need to solve a problem or take another person's perspective.

Beyond asking the right questions in the right way, students need to answer questions properly. They must give enough information, but not too much. They must stay on track and answer what was asked, not changing the topic or adding irrelevant information that could be distracting.

In evaluating the responses students gave on *TOPS 2 – Adolescent*, we considered these factors:

- **Is the answer logical?**
  Some students rattle off the first answer that comes to mind, responding impulsively vs. considering their thoughts before selecting a logical answer.

- **Is the answer the most appropriate?**
  Sometimes the answer to a question can be logical, but also uncommon. Unusual answers, even though technically correct, indicate that the student is either an atypical thinker or that the student has an unusual perspective or background knowledge. If a student consistently gives unusual, but correct, answers, he may benefit from training in selecting answers that more closely match the norm for the general population.

- **Is the vocabulary appropriately precise?**
  If the words are too general, they reflect limited vocabulary skills for adolescents, perhaps due to a small vocabulary bank, word-finding difficulties or ignorance of the quality or precision expected from adolescents.

- **Does the answer provide enough detail or specific information?**
  We expect adolescents to have enough experience in answering questions to respond with adequate information, particularly during testing or a classroom situation. Some students need training to discriminate a vague or inadequate response from a response with adequate information.

Here are some examples of questions and answers from *TOPS 2 – Adolescent* to illustrate the criteria for evaluating responses:

Question: How can people protect the rights to their inventions?

Responses: "They can keep them safe." *vague; no specific way to protect the rights*
"They can get a patent." *complete, logical, specific response*

Question: Paul, age 16, is a good student and wants a part-time job. His dad doesn't want him to work until he is 18. Why doesn't Paul look for a full-time job?

Responses: "He doesn't have time." *irrelevant; no information supporting that assumption*

"His dad doesn't want him to." *true, but ignores the comparison of a part-time vs. a full-time job*

"He has to go to school." *accurate; summarizes the major reason a full-time job is out of the question*

The tasks in this unit highlight skills related to asking and answering relevant questions appropriately.

■ Vocabulary

It is important to understand each of these words in order to think and talk about asking and answering questions.

accurate	correct, on target
appropriate	suitable, fitting
choice	something you choose; an option
clarify	to explain or make something clear/understandable
criteria	a rule or standard to evaluate or test something
describe	to represent something in words; to paint a mental picture
elaborate (v)	to expand upon what someone says
impulsive	acting or speaking without considering the consequences first
inappropriate	not correct, unacceptable
ineffective	unhelpful, useless
logical	sensible
precise	exact

Task 1

■ Use a dictionary or a thesaurus to match each word in the box with its correct synonym. Use each word only once.

expand	hasty	option	proper	standards
explain	improper	precise	reasonable	unproductive

1 accurate _____

2 appropriate _____

3 choice _____

4 clarify _____

5 criteria _____

6 elaborate _____

7 impulsive _____

8 inappropriate _____

9 ineffective _____

10 logical _____

■ Work with a partner. Take turns making complete sentences using each word in the above exercise.

Task 2

■ Play guessing games like the ones below. They are a great way to learn to ask good questions.

1 Ask a student volunteer to stand sideways to the class with his hands behind his back, ready to hold an unknown object. Show the mystery object to the class. Then place the object in the volunteer's hands. Allow the volunteer three questions to determine what the object is. After the volunteer makes a guess to identify the object, allow him to see it for himself. Then ask the class to help the student evaluate the accuracy and efficiency of the three questions he asked.

2 Another good way to boost students' skills in asking efficient questions is to play the game of 20 Questions. Place 15-30 pictures of objects faceup in front of a student or a small group of students. Tell them, "I am thinking of one of these things. You may ask me questions to figure out which one I'm thinking of, but you may only ask me questions I can answer with *yes* or *no*." (Copy and cut apart the pictures on pages 30-32 to introduce this task; then do the same task with pictures appropriate to current curricular areas.)

After each question, allow the students to turn over all pictures that have been eliminated by your answer to the question. For example, if the question was *Does it have wings?* and the answer is *no*, they would turn over each picture of something that has wings.

At first your students may ask questions that only eliminate one picture or a few pictures at a time. Model a question that would eliminate as many pictures as possible, such as *Is it something that lives?* or *Is it something man-made?* As your students ask more effective questions, limit the number of questions they may ask to ten, then to five, then to three, if possible.

3 Try the above activity with the students in your classroom. Think of one student and ask the others to ask good questions to identify the target student. (Before you present this game, remind students to be kind to each other and only make positive or neutral references to the student's appearance and characteristics.)

■ Copy these pictures and cut them apart to play guessing games.

■ Copy these pictures and cut them apart to play guessing games.

■ Copy these pictures and cut them apart to play guessing games.

If you found out there will be a new student in your class, it would be logical to ask these questions:

- Where did the new student go to school before?
- Is it a boy or a girl?
- Where will the new student sit?
- When will the new student arrive?

It would be inappropriate to ask these questions:

- Why?
- Where?
- What does the new student look like?
- Do I know the new student already?

Photo courtesy of istockphoto.com © Kurt Gordon

■ Read the paragraph and the questions. Then make a check mark beside each question that would be logical to ask about the information.

1 What foods do you think of for a traditional Thanksgiving meal? Most of us think of turkey, cranberry sauce, mashed potatoes and apple or pumpkin pie. That is not what the Pilgrims ate for their first Thanksgiving dinner, though. They may have eaten turkey, but potatoes were unknown where they lived. They had no apple trees, so they had no apple pie. If they ate cranberries, they didn't have sugar to sweeten these tart fruits. Cranberry sauce wasn't invented until about 50 years after the first Thanksgiving.

_____ **a** When did potatoes begin growing in South America?

_____ **b** What did the Pilgrims eat for the first Thanksgiving?

_____ **c** How do we know what the Pilgrims ate?

_____ **d** What time of day did the Pilgrims eat the first Thanksgiving dinner?

_____ **e** What did the Pilgrims eat for their second Thanksgiving dinner?

_____ **f** Did the Pilgrims grow pumpkins?

■ Read each paragraph and the questions. Then make a check mark beside each question that would be logical to ask about the paragraph.

2 A few Chinese merchants got rich from the California gold rush. These men took their money back to China in 1851. Within the next year, about 12,000 Chinese citizens headed for California. All but seven were men. Even 50 years later, 95% of the Chinese in the U.S. were men.

    ____ **a** How did the Chinese merchants travel back to China?

    ____ **b** Why did the Chinese merchants take their money back to China?

    ____ **c** How do we know how many people were in the U.S. during the gold rush?

    ____ **d** Why did so many more Chinese men than women come to California?

    ____ **e** Who counted the 12,000 Chinese citizens?

    ____ **f** What were the names of the seven Chinese women who came during the gold rush?

3 President Roosevelt urged Americans to be Americans first, not "hyphenated Americans." In WWI, he asked them to stop calling themselves "German-American" or "Irish-American." He said, "Once it was true that this country could not endure half American and half slave. Today it is true that it cannot endure half American and half foreign. The hyphen is incompatible with patriotism."

Photo courtesy of istockphoto.com © Jody Dingle

    ____ **a** Why didn't Roosevelt like hyphens?

    ____ **b** When was America half American and half slave?

    ____ **c** Do you think that Roosevelt would feel the same way today?

    ____ **d** What is your opinion about hyphenated terms like "Chinese-American"?

    ____ **e** Where was Roosevelt when he made this speech?

Task 4

A good answer to a question has these characteristics:

- It is true.
- It answers the question that was asked.
- It includes enough specific information.

■ Look at the picture. Then read the questions and answers. Make a check mark in front of each answer that is right on target.

1 Where are these people?

_____ **a** in an office

_____ **b** in a medical office

_____ **c** at school

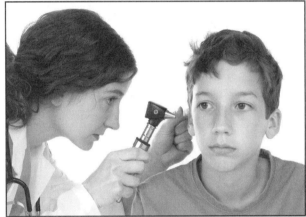

Photo courtesy of istockphoto.com © Kenneth C. Zirkel

2 What is the woman doing?

_____ **a** examining the inside of his ear

_____ **b** checking him out

_____ **c** making him feel better

3 What clues suggest that the woman has had medical training?

_____ **a** She is using a tool.

_____ **b** She is holding a medical tool.

_____ **c** She is wearing that doctor thing around her neck.

_____ **d** She is wearing a stethoscope.

_____ **e** She is wearing a white uniform.

_____ **f** Her hair is tied back away from her face.

4 How do you think the boy feels?

_____ **a** okay

_____ **b** like most people feel when a doctor checks their ears

_____ **c** He's in pain because his ear hurts.

_____ **d** He looks calm, but he might be anxious.

Comparing and Contrasting

The skill of comparing and contrasting requires that students see similar and dissimilar attributes of an object, situation or person. Often, teachers make writing assignments based on comparing and contrasting certain things or ideas. This kind of an assignment encourages critical thinking by requiring students to go beyond mere description or summary to generate interesting analyses. Reflecting on similarities and differences helps students gain deeper understanding of the items to be compared.

Sometimes students need to use graphic organizers to help with the task of comparing and contrasting. A Venn diagram works well to show similarities and differences and commonalities. A T-Chart also works well because a student can list the characteristics of an object down the center column and then put the similarities in the left column and the differences in the right column.

To help students get started on the task of understanding the importance of comparing and contrasting, ask them the following questions about two common objects—a pen and a pencil. Put their answers, and any other relevant information, in a Venn diagram.

What is done with each one?	*writing, drawing*
What is contained in each one?	*lead in a pencil, ink in a pen*
What is on the outside of each one?	*wood on a pencil, plastic on a pen*
Where would you find each one?	*desk drawer, cup, pocket, purse, etc.*
Who uses them?	*all people able to hold them*
When do you use each one?	*when something needs to be written or drawn*

Now, have the students tell you three of the six questions and answers above that are the most important when talking about pens and pencils. They will probably decide that the first three are what *distinguishes* a pen from a pencil, and that's the point of comparing and contrasting!

■ Vocabulary

It is important to understand each of these words in order to think and talk about comparing and contrasting.

analyze	to think about the parts or features of something to help you understand how it works
attribute (n)	an inherent characteristic or quality of something
category	a distinct group or class to which objects or concepts belong
characteristic	a specific quality that distinguishes or identifies one person, thing or class from another
compare	to examine two things and determine how they are alike
composition	what an object is made of
compromise	to make adjustments in what you want in order to reach agreement with someone
contrast	to pick out differences between and among people, places, things or ideas
describe	to represent something in words; to paint a mental picture
differences	ways things or ideas are unlike
disagreement	two or more people having different opinions about the same issue
distinguish	to perceive a difference between and among people, places, things or ideas
divided	disagreeing with each other
function	what an object does or is used for
mediator	a neutral person who listens to both sides and renders a decision to resolve a conflict
relevant	relating to what is being discussed or considered; pertinent
separate (v)	to make a distinction between and among people, places, things or ideas
similarities	ways things or ideas are alike

Task 1

■ Choose the best word from the box to complete each sentence or question. Use each word only once.

analyze	compromise	disagreement	function
characteristics	describe	distinguish	mediator
compare	difference	divided	relevant

1 It is important to _____ all of the information before making a decision.

2 Evan and Bryan had a _____ about how to play the game.

3 As part of your biology project, you must _____ the growth of the plants.

4 Sometimes it is necessary for a _____ to resolve a conflict.

5 What is the _____ of a gyroscope?

6 Knowing how to _____ is helpful when you and a friend are trying to make a decision.

7 When writing a report about something, only include the most _____ information.

8 Mr. Conner drew a chart to show the _____ in each country's population.

9 Isabelle's grandma couldn't _____ any difference between the cookies Isabelle made and the cookies her sister made.

10 On the test, students had to list at least three _____ to describe the hero in the story.

11 The class was _____ about where to donate the money they raised.

12 At the Invention Convention, each student had two minutes to _____ his invention.

Comparing and Contrasting
Tasks Of Problem Solving – Adolescent   **38**   Copyright © 2007 LinguiSystems, Inc.

Task 2

■ Tell one way the people in each pair are the same. Then tell one way they are different.

1 veterinarian / doctor

2 clown / magician

3 nurse / doctor

4 mail carrier / UPS driver

5 firefighter / police officer

6 taxi driver / bus driver

7 school principal / teacher

8 dentist / doctor

9 mechanic / plumber

10 painter / sculptor

11 baby / toddler

12 author / songwriter

13 judge / lawyer

14 mother / father

15 niece / nephew

16 teller / cashier

17 salesperson / waiter

18 chef / bartender

19 pilot / flight attendant

20 brother / sister

Task 3

■ Choose a word or phrase from the box to answer each question.

blood pressure cuff	helmet	mallet	stethoscope
border collie	instrument	screwdriver	sweeping the floor
brushing teeth	liberty	shin guards	tongue depressor
Christianity	lobster	St. Bernard	typing
clam	making music	statue	wrench

1   What do you use to remove a bolt?

_____

What do you use to remove a screw?

_____

2   What does a football player wear during a football game?

_____

What does a soccer player wear during a soccer game?

_____

3   What does a doctor use to check your heart?

_____

What does a doctor use to check your reflexes?

_____

4   What does a nurse use to check your blood pressure?

_____

What does a nurse use to check your throat?

_____

5   What shellfish has claws?

_____

What shellfish has a hinged shell that opens and closes?

_____

6   What dog is bred to rescue people in snow?

_____

What dog is bred to herd sheep?

_____

7   What does a sculptor sculpt?

_____

What does a musician play?

_____

8   What does the statue on an island in the Hudson River in New York stand for?

_____

What does a cross stand for?

_____

9   What is a piano keyboard for?

_____

What is a computer keyboard for?

_____

10   What is a broom for?

_____

What is a toothbrush for?

_____

Task 4

■ Each sentence pair on the left goes with two of the statements on the right. Write the number of each sentence pair next to one statement that compares the two sentences and one statement that contrasts them.

1   Haley went to the salon.
    Harry went to the barber.

2   Junior's mom enrolled him in preschool.
    Carrie enrolled in college.

3   Rick closed the bedroom door.
    Linda closed the living room drapes.

4   Jane hid Easter eggs for her grandchildren.
    Dan hid the gift for his wife.

5   Mr. Sullivan assigned math homework.
    Ms. Smith assigned history homework.

6   Chris rode his motorcycle.
    Sarah rode her tricycle.

7   Lisa carried a purse.
    Larry carried a backpack.

8   He bought a six-pack of soda.
    She bought a bag of chips.

9   Jamie skied behind the boat.
    Jason skied down the slopes.

10 Mom ate salmon.
    Dad ate a hamburger.

_____ They rode something.

_____ She was playing a game;
he was trying to keep a secret.

_____ She went water-skiing;
he went snow skiing.

_____ They assigned homework.

_____ She carried personal items;
he carried school items.

_____ They ate something.

_____ He teaches math;
she teaches history.

_____ They went skiing.

_____ They bought something.

_____ They went to get haircuts.

_____ They wanted privacy.

_____ She ate fish; he ate beef.

_____ They went to different places.

_____ He was in the bedroom;
she was in the living room.

_____ He rode something motorized;
she pedaled.

_____ He bought something to drink;
she bought something to eat.

_____ They enrolled in school.

_____ They hid something.

_____ He is a young boy;
she is a teenager.

_____ They carried something.

Task 5

■ Choose words from the box to complete these sentences correctly. Use each answer only once.

water is away from the shore	**moon**	**water is close to the shore**
photos	**air waves**	**sun**
United States	**Arctic**	**Argentina**
Antarctic	**gases**	**earth**

1 The moon gets its light from the _____.

2 The sun gets its light from _____.

3 A satellite receives _____.

4 A radio telescope receives _____.

5 A high tide means _____.

6 A low tide means _____.

7 The South Pole is called the _____.

8 The North Pole is called the _____.

9 The Northern Hemisphere has the _____ in its boundaries.

10 The Southern Hemisphere has _____ in its boundaries.

11 A solar eclipse is caused by the _____.

12 A lunar eclipse is caused by the _____.

■ Choose words from the box to complete these sentences correctly. Use each answer only once.

darkness	light	Venus
dirty snowballs	oval	where to migrate
disk with arm	pay attention to impulses	
falling stars	Pluto	

1 There are times in the winter that some countries have continual _____.

2 There are times in the summer when some countries have nearly continual

   _____.

3 Instinct tells creatures _____.

4 Instinct tells humans to _____.

5 The planet closest to Earth is _____.

6 The planet farthest from Earth is _____.

7 Meteorites are often called _____.

8 Comets are often called _____.

9 Elliptical galaxies are shaped like an _____.

10 Spiral galaxies are shaped like a _____.

Task 7

■ Circle the sentence in each pair that is false.

1 Pollution is caused by people.
Pollution is caused by the Earth's rotation.

2 Wetlands are named for lands that have swimming pools.
Wetlands are names for areas with continual surface water.

3 Cleaning products cause water pollution.
Automobiles cause soil pollution.

4 Electricity is more polluting than gasoline.
Gasoline is more polluting than ethanol.

5 An ecosystem is made up of both living and non-living things.
An ecosystem is made up of only plants and animals.

6 Ecosystems can be destroyed by man.
Ecosystems can be destroyed by animals.

7 Herbivores eat soil.
Carnivores eat meat.

8 Grasslands cannot be restored after damage.
Grasslands are found on every continent except Antarctica.

9 Coral reefs are living organisms.
Coral reefs cannot be damaged by SCUBA divers.

10 Farmers rotate crops to reenergize the soil.
Farmers rotate crops to relieve boredom.

11 Most animals use tools.
Man is the only animal that uses tools.

12 Most animals communicate.
Man is the only animal that communicates.

Task 8a

■ Read the story and answer the questions.

Jeremy and Bill have been best friends since kindergarten. They are juniors in high school and are enjoying their independence now that they both drive. Jeremy gets to drive to school but Bill has to ride the bus. Bill gets to drive to his job after school but Jeremy has to walk.

The two boys' parents are very different. Jeremy's parents trust him to be a careful driver. Bill's parents do not trust him to drive carefully. Both sets of parents worry about their sons when they're driving but they worry more if they are driving with each other.

1 Why do you think Jeremy's parents trust him to be a careful driver?

_____

_____

2 Why do you think Bill's parents do not trust him to be a careful driver?

_____

_____

3 Why does Jeremy get to drive to school?

_____

_____

4 Why does Bill get to drive to work?

_____

_____

5 Why do the boys' parents worry when the boys drive with each other?

_____

_____

■ Read the story and answer the questions.

Are you a cat or a dog lover? Alicia loves all kinds of pets. Her favorites are dogs and cats. She prefers dogs because they are loyal and smart and because they learn tricks easily when they are young. Alicia likes cats because they are independent. Alicia knows that every pet has its own personality, even her gerbils and geckos. Her gerbils are curious and busy. Her geckos spend most of their time lying in the sun.

1 Why do you think dogs are more loyal than cats?

_____

_____

2 Why do you think cats are more independent than dogs?

_____

_____

3 Why do you think Alicia likes gerbils?

_____

_____

4 Why do you think she likes geckos?

_____

_____

5 Why are dogs better able to learn tricks when they are young?

_____

_____

Identifying Problems

The tasks in this unit highlight identifying problems, expressing them clearly and determining the urgency of problems.

Using clear, specific language to state a problem lays the foundation for addressing the problem effectively. Pre-teach and use the words on page 48 as you and your students discuss problems to enhance the clarity of both thinking and talking about problems.

Explain to your students that many problems can be stated well in more than one way. Demonstrate this fact by restating problems your students have identified, and also ask your students to share their answers for the tasks in this unit to note how similar thoughts can be expressed clearly in different ways. This practice reminds students that language is flexible and there is often more than one "correct" way to state a problem or express our thoughts.

The tasks in this unit present common problems your students encounter. The general task is for your students to state the problem in their own words. As your students complete the tasks, encourage them to work in pairs and/or to share their answers so everyone can learn from each other. Also ask your students to express the clues that helped them to identify the known or potential problems in given situations. Here are some additional activities to help your students practice identifying problems.

1 Use real-life situations and pictures as much as possible to teach your students to identify and state problems clearly. Since most of your students are becoming increasingly aware of local, national and world events and concerns, news articles are especially relevant to discussions about problems.

2 Keep a classroom list of problems your school faces, such as a lack of computers, vandalism or schedule conflicts. Talk with your students about each problem before working as a group to describe it clearly for your list. Use the board or an overhead as you brainstorm and refine ways to capture the problem with appropriate wording.

3 Talk about the problems in story plots. Help your students word these problems clearly and write the problems on an overhead or the board.

4 Talk about the problems students have with specific assignments or situations. Here are some examples:

- There aren't enough copies of the book we all need to read for our report.
- Many students plagiarize when they do assignments or write reports.

5 Model clear statements of problems you encounter and restate students' concerns or problems as clearly as possible.

■ Vocabulary

It is important to understand each of these words in order to think and talk about identifying problems.

cause	the reason something happened; what made something happen
clarify	to explain or make something clear/understandable
consider	to examine; to think about
describe	to represent something in words; to paint a mental picture
dilemma	a problem with no easy solution
drawback	a disadvantage about a situation or a solution to a problem
elaborate (v)	to expand upon what someone says
evidence	facts, proof
explain	to describe how or why something works or is true
identify	to point out or recognize something
issue (n)	a problem, a situation, a topic to think about
paraphrase	to restate a message in different words
problem	a challenge to solve
restate	to paraphrase or repeat what someone said
suspicion	a feeling or guess that something is a problem, someone did something or something happened
urgent	needing immediate action or attention

■ Choose words from the box to complete these sentences correctly. Use each word only once.

cause	describe	drawback	evidence	paraphrase	suspicion
consider	dilemma	elaborate	issues	problem	urgent

1 What _____ do you have that the problem still exists?

2 A _____ is just a challenge you need to manage.

3 _____ the consequences before you decide what to do.

4 If a situation is _____, it requires immediate attention.

5 A _____ of using a permanent marker is that it can stain your clothes.

6 What are the most important _____ facing your local government?

7 Let me _____ what you just said to make sure I understand what you mean.

8 What was the major _____ of spreading the flu epidemic?

9 I have a _____ that my teacher doesn't like me.

10 My _____ is that I won't perform well if I don't practice, but if I practice, I won't have time to do my assignments.

11 Please _____ the current situation as clearly as you can.

12 If people don't understand what you mean, you might need to _____ on what you already told them.

■ Compare the meanings of the words in each pair.

1 clarify – explain
2 restate – paraphrase
3 suspicion – evidence
4 problem – dilemma

■ Look at these pictures. Then identify at least one problem in each picture.

1

_____

_____

_____

_____

_____

_____

2

_____

_____

_____

_____

_____

■ Look at these pictures. Then identify at least one problem in each picture.

1

_____

_____

_____

_____

_____

2

_____

_____

_____

_____

_____

■ Look at these pictures. Then identify at least one problem in each picture.

1

_____

_____

_____

_____

_____

_____

2

_____

_____

_____

_____

_____

_____

Task 3a

■ Read the caption below each picture. Then tell at least one problem for the person in the picture.

1

Mrs. Jenkins, a secretary from 1935-1942, tries a computer keyboard for the first time.

_____

_____

_____

_____

_____

_____

2

The rider flies off the handlebars.

_____

_____

_____

_____

_____

_____

■ Read the caption below each picture. Then tell at least one problem for the people involved.

1

signs greet vacationing family at the beach

_____

_____

_____

_____

_____

_____

2

sunburned swimmers retreat from the beach

_____

_____

_____

_____

_____

_____

■ Read each situation and answer the questions.

1 Nate is taking care of his young cousins. He told his aunt he has an appointment at 4:30, so he could only watch the boys until 4:00. It is now 4:40 and his aunt hasn't come home yet.

   a What is Nate's biggest problem?

   _____

   b Why doesn't Nate let the kids take care of themselves until their mom returns?

   _____

   c What might be a reason the mom hasn't come home yet?

   _____

2 Brad has missed school often due to illness this year, and his grades have slipped. His mom is trying to restrict his diet to healthy foods only. Brad would rather have cookies or crackers than fruit.

   a What is Brad's problem with food?

   _____

   b What is Brad's problem with school?

   _____

   c What might be causing Brad's poor health?

   _____

■ Read each situation. Then state the problem clearly.

1 Eli, Rashid, Jen and James were asked to work as a team to do a science project. Each time they get together, the boys crack jokes about the way Jen looks and they don't take the project seriously. Jen hopes to get into a good college and doesn't want a bad grade.

What are two problems for Jen?

_____

_____

2 Emma agreed to take care of a neighbor's collie while the neighbor went on vacation. While Emma walked the dog today, it pulled the leash from her hand and ran away.

What is Emma's problem?

_____

3 You and your friends play ball on an empty lot down the street. Now the lot owner is building a parking structure on the lot.

What is your problem?

_____

4 You want to spend Saturday with your friends, but your dad wants you to spend the day with him.

What is your problem?

_____

5 Shawna's mom asked her to clean her room before she got together with her friends. Shawna left when she thought her room was clean enough. When she got home, her mom was angry because she didn't think Shawna's room was clean.

What is Shawna's problem?

_____

6 Tony is trying to do his homework. His brother shares a room with him and is playing loud music and practicing his drums.

What is Tony's problem?

_____

Task 6

Read about each situation and follow the directions.

1 Adel's dog, Mandy, has been her dog since she got her as a puppy when she was three. Mandy is old now and can hardly walk because of severe arthritis. Sometimes she can't even stand up. Mandy also has painful digestion problems and the vet says it will only get worse. Adel needs to decide whether to have Mandy put to sleep or to keep her until she dies.

Write the benefit and the drawback for each solution to Adel's problem.

a She lets the vet put Mandy to sleep.

Benefit   _____

Drawback   _____

b She keeps Mandy until she dies.

Benefit   _____

Drawback   _____

2 Ray's dad is strict about lights out after 10:00. There is no way Ray can finish his homework before his bedtime. If Ray studies for his math test, he will do well on the test. If he doesn't finish his paper for language arts, he will get a 0 for 15% of his grade this quarter.

Write the drawback for each solution to Ray's problem.

a He could just study for the math test.

_____

b He could just finish his language arts report.

_____

c He could do part of the report and spend half the time studying for the math test.

_____

How could Ray have avoided this problem?

_____

Detecting Key Information

Our brains receive much more information about what we read or experience than we really need. The better we can detect which data is critical for our purposes, the more efficiently we can process the information and take appropriate action.

Students who do not focus on key information are at a disadvantage in academic tasks such as summarizing, taking notes and answering written test questions. These students are easily distracted and even overwhelmed with the amount of information they attempt to process. Guided instruction can help these students zero in on the essential information to think about for a specific purpose.

Alert your students that just because information is true doesn't mean it is relevant to a topic. For example, if you give directions for making microwave popcorn, a comment about where you buy your favorite popcorn is irrelevant to the directions. Teach your students to ask themselves, "Is this piece of information about the topic? If not, it's irrelevant. If so, is it essential or nonessential?" Use the graphic organizer on page 61 to help your students visualize prioritizing information according to its relevancy to a topic.

Outlining a class lesson or a textbook chapter is another great way to focus attention on prioritizing the importance of information. More important information is usually on the left-hand side on an outline; related, but less important, information is further to the right. Irrelevant information is omitted entirely.

The tasks in this unit begin at a sentence level and proceed to longer passages. For students with weaker skills, present these tasks by reading them aloud as your students read along with you. For students more proficient in detecting key information in a written form, present the tasks orally without having your students read along. This level more closely resembles the classroom situation.

Either way you present the tasks in this unit, have your students explain their reasoning for selecting appropriate responses. This technique helps your students clarify their thinking and gives them valuable practice in expressing their reasoning to others.

Other activities that enhance skills in detecting key information include:

1 Identifying the main ideas of school announcements, textbook readings and stories.

2 Outlining textbook chapters or the steps to do something. Compare students' outlines to see what information most students consider essential vs. nonessential.

3 Asking your students to identify the key information in song lyrics, news articles and political announcements or speeches.

58

■ Vocabulary

It is important to understand each of these words in order to think and talk about detecting key information.

analyze   to think about the parts or features of something to help you understand how it works

current situation   what is happening now

detect   to notice or discover something; to identify

evidence   facts, proof

irrelevant   not important for a certain purpose; unrelated; beside the point

issue (n)   a problem; a situation; a topic to think about

organize   to arrange things thoughtfully and logically

outline (n)   a list of the main points of an article, a report or a lecture

prioritize   to sequence things according to their importance or need for immediate attention

summarize   to repeat information briefly, keeping the main ideas and leaving out the details

■ Choose words from the box to complete these sentences correctly. Use each word only once.

analyze	detect	irrelevant	organize	prioritize
current	evidence	issue	outline	summarize

1 Making an _____ of a chapter is a good way to learn the information.

2 What _____ was found at the crime scene?

3 The _____ weather situation makes driving dangerous.

4 A good detective can quickly _____ key facts or clues.

5 We used a microscope to _____ the structure of the cells.

6 Please _____ your report with one sentence.

7 What is the main _____ in the election?

8 Nurses in an emergency room need to _____ their patients for medical treatment.

9 "What you did instead of doing your homework is _____ to me," said Mrs. Gibbon.

10 Please _____ all of your tools and chemicals before you begin your experiment.

Key information about a topic is important. It is what you need to know. It is essential.

Related information about a topic is true, but it isn't important to know. It is nonessential.

Irrelevant information is unimportant. It might not even be about the topic.

■ Use this diagram to sort key information from related or irrelevant information.

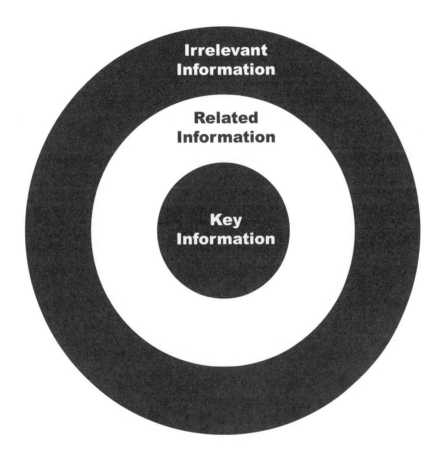

Key information is the bull's-eye of the target. It is essential or necessary to know for the topic or purpose.

Related information is about the topic, but it isn't essential for the topic or purpose.

Irrelevant information is information you don't need that isn't about the specific topic or purpose.

Task 3

■ Identify the sentence that doesn't give relevant information about the topic.

1 It will take me an hour to do my homework tonight. It rained today. I'll start my homework at 4:00.

2 Tracy sits next to me in Spanish. I'm excited about Saturday. Our club is having a car wash in the parking lot of Ryan's Lumber.

3 Do you have an extra pencil? I forgot to bring one today. Chad's stepmom bakes really good cookies.

4 Maria is in training for track. She jogs eight miles a day. We had a great track team last year.

5 The weather forecast predicts that the hurricane will be a Level 4 when it hits land. It's already 3:00. All the residents of the barrier islands need to evacuate immediately.

6 We're going swimming at the community pool. I'm so hungry! Remember to bring a beach towel.

7 Have you seen my book bag? We have a geometry test today. I hope the test is easier than the last one was.

8 Make sure you have all the parts before you assemble the model. I hate the smell of the glue. Follow each direction in order and check each step before you go on to the next direction.

9 Kelsey wants to be a veterinarian. She's always taking care of hurt animals. It's almost time to go home.

10 Call me on my cell tonight. What's that noise? We can do our science homework together by phone.

11 For my science project, I'm doing tests on drinking water. I'm going to use tap water and different brands of bottled water. I think I'm getting a cold.

12 Go two blocks south. I heard about Steph and Dave. Then turn right on Hansen and look for the big red sign.

Task 4

■ Identify the two sentences in each group that include key information about the topic.

1 The monarch butterfly follows a migration pattern that covers many miles. Interestingly, no one butterfly makes a round-trip migration. It is too cold in Antarctica to grow milkweed.

Photo courtesy of istockphoto.com © Nikola Bilic

2 The Golden Gate Bridge was built in just four years. I've been across it many times. The bridge opened to traffic in 1937.

3 Our class is selling wrapping paper to raise money. My favorite is the one with sports equipment. We're hoping to buy new basketballs with the money we raise.

4 A puggle is a new breed of dog. I used to have a dog. A puggle is a mix of a pug and a beagle.

5 Biting your fingernails is a dirty habit that can make you sick. It puts germs right into your mouth. You should try my easy recipe for fudge.

6 Grant's Tomb is much more than the place where President Grant was entombed. It has many cultural events, including musket firing demonstrations with period costumes. Many people like to visit Washington, D.C. in the springtime.

7 The Canadian flag has a maple leaf. Why do the stars on the U.S. flag have five points instead of six? Betsy Ross, who sewed the first flag for George Washington, told him five-pointed stars were easier to stitch.

8 Mount Rushmore is the world's largest one-piece sculpture. Pennsylvania has many hiking trails. Few people realize that the artist died before his sculpture was finished.

9 I'm going on a diet this week. The Statue of Liberty is a colossal symbol of freedom and democracy. Her face is over eight feet tall and her waist is 35 feet.

10 There are many superstitions about the ladybug. We have lots of them in our garden this year. In Sweden, if a ladybug lands on a maiden's hand, she will soon be married.

Task 5

■ These are steps to do projects. Identify the steps that are irrelevant for each project.

1 Pizza Delivery

_____ Some pizzas are spicier than others.
_____ Decide what kind of pizza you want to order.
_____ Find the phone number of the pizzeria you prefer.
_____ Call the pizzeria and order your pizza.
_____ Most pizzas are round but some are square.
_____ Be ready to pay the delivery person when your pizza arrives.
_____ Tip the deliverer.

Photo courtesy of istockphoto.com © Lisa F. Young

2 Chicago Hot Dog

_____ Boil or steam a Vienna Beef hot dog.
_____ Place the cooked hot dog into a poppy seed hot dog bun.
_____ Some people prefer plain buns, but I prefer poppy seed buns.
_____ Drizzle mustard on top of the hot dog.
_____ Add chopped onions, sweet pickle relish, a dill pickle spear and chopped tomato.
_____ You need to be hungry to eat one of these.
_____ Add sport pepper and a dash of celery salt, but do not add ketchup.

3 Repotting a Plant

_____ Make sure the new pot is slightly larger than the pot the plant is in now.
_____ Put some charcoal or small pebbles in the bottom of the new pot.
_____ Some plants need watering more often than others.
_____ Turn the plant upside down and let it fall into your hand gently.
_____ Turn the plant right-side up and set it in the new pot.
_____ Fill the gap between the old dirt and the new pot with fresh potting soil.
_____ Tap the soil to make the surface even.
_____ Ivy is one of the hardiest house plants.
_____ Water the plant.

4 Doing Laundry

_____ Sort the dirty laundry by color and washing needs.
_____ Put detergent into the washer.
_____ Do you do your own laundry?
_____ Place one load of clothes into the washer.
_____ Set the controls for water level, temperature and washing speed.
_____ Start the washer.
_____ Our washer takes about 25 minutes to do one load.

Task 6

■ Identify the most important information in each sentence.

1 Carla, my cousin, broke her leg while she was skating with her friends.

2 The picnic starts at 11:00 a.m., but if you don't want to be there on time, we can go at noon.

3 One ticket costs $5 and you can get a discount if you buy 10 for $40.

4 I had no cavities at my checkup, but the dental hygienist said that I need to brush my teeth more carefully.

5 We usually take the bus to go to the museum, but today we're driving because we need to bring a stroller for my aunt's baby.

6 Grandma's favorite winter sweater has a hole in it from moths.

7 I need a pencil for the math test because mine fell out of my pocket.

8 Candidate Nelson promised to cut taxes, increase the minimum wage and cure cancer if he wins the election.

9 I ordered a gift for Grandpa online, but I didn't pay extra for gift wrapping, so please put a bow on the package for me, Grandma.

10 When we have good weather, our dog, T-Rex, likes to dig holes in the lot next door to our building.

11 Derek got a rash on his face from his new glasses because they have metal rims, and he has an allergy to the nickel in some metals.

Imagine you are the judge in a trial. It is your responsibility to decide which evidence is key or relevant to the case and which evidence is not relevant.

The case is about shoplifting. The accused, Diana, is charged with stealing eight cashmere sweaters from Swift Department Store on the afternoon of Tuesday, March 4th.

■ Make a check mark beside each piece of information that is relevant to this case. Then explain why it is relevant.

_____ **1** Diana is 15 years old.

_____

_____ **2** Mrs. Perry, store detective, saw Diana leave the store, carrying a large shopping bag that looked full.

_____

_____ **3** Diana is allergic to cashmere.

_____

_____ **4** It is Diana's birthday tomorrow.

_____

_____ **5** Diana has signed permission to use her mother's charge card.

_____

_____ **6** Diana sometimes sells things on the Internet.

_____

_____ **7** Diana had a receipt in her purse for the eight sweaters. They were charged to her mother.

_____

_____ **8** Diana's mother had a printout of the list of sweaters she asked Diana to buy for her to give as gifts to relatives.

_____

■ Identify the key information in this article. Explain why you think each piece of information you identify is key to understanding the article.

Hamming Around

On Sunday, over 300 people gathered in Pine Run for the 37th annual Pine Run Ham Radio Amateur Club Flea Market. Shoppers and traders came from all over New England for this event. Bert Graff, who organized the event, said, "It was a big success, but we get fewer people every year. It's a shame. I've been active in this group for over 40 years. I just wish more young people would take up this hobby. Our group will die out without more young folks."

The government depends on ham operators to help when the Internet is down. When Hurricane Katrina brought down communication towers in 2005, ham operators were a key source of communication.

The Pine Run event included computers and other modern electronic devices to draw more young people. "It's tough competing with high-tech devices," noted Graff. "Most kids think things that were invented before the computer are dull and useless. We want them to know that's not true."

Photo courtesy of istockphoto.com © Bradford Shearer

Barney Clark spent all day at the event. "It's easy to be a ham operator," he said. "You take a test on electronics and how to run a ham radio station. If you pass, you get a license with your own call letters." Clark plans to campaign at local high schools next year. He hopes he will be able to recruit some young ham operators.

■ These are letters to an advice columnist. Identify the key information in each letter. Explain why each piece of information you identify is essential to understand the author's situation.

1 *Dear Carla,*

I've been best friends with Sharon for eight years. We've grown up together. We've shared our deepest thoughts and feelings about everything. We've been there for each other through good times and sad times. I thought we would always be best friends.

One month ago, Sharon started dating Roy. Now she spends all her time with him. I never hear from her. I'm lost without her. How can I get my best friend back again?
Lonely

2 *Dear Carla,*

I think I'm my own worst enemy. I buy whatever I want, not whatever I need. Whenever I see anything I'd like to have, I buy it.

I have a decent allowance and I earn some money babysitting. It's just that I buy things that I don't need. I'm usually sorry afterwards. I tell myself what a greedy, out-of-control person I am. Will I always be this way? What if I start buying more expensive things? I have no clue how I can stop this ugly habit.
Big Spender

3 *Dear Carla,*

I've always done well in sports. Last year, I was on the school soccer, basketball and baseball teams. That took a lot of my time and I wanted to keep my grades up, so I quit basketball this year. My parents and my coach keep telling me they are disappointed. They think I have real talent for sports and they don't think I should have quit.

I love sports, but now that I'm in high school, I want to try other activities, too, like photography and chess club. How can I persuade my parents and teachers to let me make my own choices? I want to learn from my own mistakes. I don't want my life to revolve around just sports and classes. I want to try new activities to help explore a future career. Can you give me any advice?
Struggling

Making Inferences

It is important to distinguish between observations and inferences. Anything that can be experienced directly, such as sights, sounds, smells and touch are observations. Inferences, though, are things one does to the observation, such as conclude, explain or decide. An inference may or may not be correct, and it is this correctness that separates an observation from an inference.

To further distinguish their differences, an observation is the cognizance of some condition and an inference is the result of a mental exercise that tries to explain something about an observation. For example, if you see white matter in the sky behind a mountain, you might think that it's a cloud. That would be an observation because it was an awareness of a condition. Your friend, though, looks differently at the white matter and notes that the mountain is Mount Saint Helens. She then applies what she knows about that mountain (that it continues to erupt occasionally) and suggests that it may be smoke from an eruption. That's an inference because the friend applied extra knowledge that was not observable to the vision. Another friend wonders if it could be smoke from a brush fire in the valley. That's another inference because that friend is wondering if last night's fire had been fully extinguished.

A good way to test if an inference is true is to ask "If . . . then" questions. "If that white blob in the sky is smoke, then why is it only white and not shades of gray?" or "If that's smoke from St. Helens, then why haven't we heard that it's erupting again on the news today?"

Here are some questions to ask your students to get them into the habit of looking "deeper" at something seemingly obvious.

When you first saw (heard, tasted, felt) this, what did you think it was?

- What else could it be?
- What was its cause?
- What do you know about that's similar?
- Do you think where you saw it affected how you observed it?
- Do you think the time of day you saw it affected how you observed it?

■ Vocabulary

It is important to understand each of these words in order to think and talk about making inferences.

cognizance	knowledge; awareness
conclude	to reach a decision after thinking something through; to finish
decide	to take a position after deliberation
deduce	to reason about cause and effect
differentiate	to distinguish between two things
explain	to describe how or why something works or is true
express	to communicate your beliefs, opinions and knowledge
imply	to make a deduction
infer	to draw a conclusion based on what you see or hear
observe	to watch carefully; to notice
reason (v)	to think logically and coherently
similarities	ways things or ideas are alike
situation	a condition in which you find yourself

■ Choose words from the box to complete these sentences correctly. Use each word only once.

concluded	differentiate	express	observe	similarity
decide	explain	imply	reasoned	situation

1 Sometimes it's hard to _____ between right and wrong.

2 There is a very strong _____ between you and your sister.

3 I went to _____ the first grade class today so I could be a tutor.

4 "I didn't mean to _____ that you were cheating," said his teacher.

5 She needed to _____ her grief to someone.

6 I don't want to be put in an awkward _____.

7 I _____ out the answer to the math problem.

8 When I say I don't understand, that means you need to _____ it to me.

9 After reviewing the evidence, the jury _____ that the defendant was innocent.

10 She needs to _____ between the blue and pink sweaters.

■ Tell how the words in each pair are associated.

1 reason – infer
2 express – explain
3 imply – deduce
4 conclude – decide

Task 2

■ Read each situation. Then make a check mark in front of the correct answer.

1 Mia bought sandpaper, paint remover, paint and a brush. What was Mia about to do?

_____ **a** build a bookshelf
_____ **b** refinish a bookshelf
_____ **c** dust a bookshelf

2 The beaver colony gathered branches, twigs, leaves and mud. What was the colony getting ready to do?

_____ **a** build a dam
_____ **b** build a river bank
_____ **c** build a deck

3 Norm doesn't wear glasses or contacts anymore. What happened?

_____ **a** His eyes got better on their own.
_____ **b** He still can't see well but doesn't want to wear eye correction.
_____ **c** He had eye surgery to improve his vision.

4 Gregory doesn't play halfback anymore. Now he plays running back. What happened?

_____ **a** He couldn't remember all of the plays.
_____ **b** His running has improved.
_____ **c** both of the above

5 Lisa gathered up the diaper, lotion, towel, soap and shampoo. What was she about to do?

_____ **a** take a bath
_____ **b** give the baby a bath
_____ **c** change the baby's diaper

6 Seven-year-old Cameron is excited. He can only go 10 miles per hour, but he needs to wear a helmet and stay out of the streets. What is Cameron doing?

_____ **a** riding a motorcycle
_____ **b** pushing a stroller
_____ **c** riding a motorized scooter

7 Emily answered the phone, made an appointment, sent a FAX and bought lunch. Who is Emily?

_____ **a** an office assistant
_____ **b** a mail clerk
_____ **c** a nurse

Task 3

■ Read each situation. Then make a check mark in front of the correct answer.

1 Roy opened the hood, took out the carburetor, replaced the spark plugs and filled the washer fluid. Who is Roy?

_____ **a** a janitor
_____ **b** a mechanic
_____ **c** a surgeon

2 Motors roared, tires screeched and pit crews worked with lightning speed. Where were we?

_____ **a** a race track
_____ **b** a parking lot
_____ **c** a highway

3 She weighs him, measures his height, takes his blood pressure and checks his reflexes. Who is she?

_____ **a** a librarian
_____ **b** a nurse
_____ **c** an equestrian

4 She uses scissors, a comb and a dryer. Who is she?

_____ **a** a seamstress
_____ **b** a tailor
_____ **c** a hairstylist

5 He thought of a plot, a theme, characters and details. Who is he?

_____ **a** an author
_____ **b** a writer
_____ **c** both of the above

6 She made a medical breakthrough by inspecting the details contained in DNA. Who is she?

_____ **a** a police officer
_____ **b** a detective
_____ **c** a scientist

7 He preps his station with a sharp knife, seasonings and several cutting boards. Who is he?

_____ **a** a farmer
_____ **b** a chef
_____ **c** a waiter

Task 4

■ Read each situation. Then make a check mark in front of the correct answer.

1 He gathered his nets, traps and coolers. What does he do?

_____ **a** fishes
_____ **b** plays basketball
_____ **c** hunts deer

2 She puts on her practice leotards and pointed shoes, puts her hair in a ponytail and stands by the bar. What does she do?

_____ **a** bartends
_____ **b** dances
_____ **c** gymnastics

3 He wears a uniform with a hat, carries a case full of maps and checks out his vehicle before boarding. What does he do?

_____ **a** drives a truck
_____ **b** operates a backhoe
_____ **c** flies a plane

4 She watches her students run around the course 20 times and looks at her stopwatch occasionally. Who is she?

_____ **a** a track coach
_____ **b** a soccer coach
_____ **c** a softball coach

5 He hauls tar paper, shingles, a hammer and nails from his truck to the house. Who is he?

_____ **a** a carpenter
_____ **b** a roofer
_____ **c** a plumber

6 They work in towers, help with navigation and ensure safety. Who are they?

_____ **a** air traffic controllers
_____ **b** lighthouse keepers
_____ **c** pilots

7 I stand before an audience and try to make them laugh. Who am I?

_____ **a** an undertaker
_____ **b** a comedian
_____ **c** a teacher

Task 5

■ Read each situation. Then make a check mark in front of the correct answer.

1 Megan caught the bus and transferred to the subway. Where was Megan?

_____   **a** in a city
_____   **b** in a suburb
_____   **c** in a town

2 They don't use telephones or anything with engines. Who are they?

_____   **a** native Americans
_____   **b** skateboarders
_____   **c** the Amish

3 Everyone sang the National Anthem and sat on the bleachers outside. Where were they?

_____   **a** a basketball game
_____   **b** a baseball game
_____   **c** a wrestling match

4 Hazel grabbed a basket and ran down the aisles putting things in it. Where was Hazel?

_____   **a** a gas station
_____   **b** a church
_____   **c** a grocery store

5 She wore a net over her head and face and clothing from head to toe. Who was she?

_____   **a** a fashion model
_____   **b** a beekeeper
_____   **c** a dancer

6 It fishes for food and hibernates in a cave. What is it?

_____   **a** a wolf
_____   **b** a bear
_____   **c** a coyote

7 It fishes for food and lives in a colony. What is it?

_____   **a** a penguin
_____   **b** an ant
_____   **c** an alligator

■ Read each situation. Then make a check mark in front of the correct answer.

1 She stood in the assembly line, put on the fender and fastened the bolts. Where is she?

____ **a** an airport
____ **b** a factory
____ **c** a car dealership

2 The puck hit the Plexiglas. Where are we?

____ **a** a hockey game
____ **b** a soccer game
____ **c** a baseball game

3 We took a stroll on the deck and then went to our cabin for the night. Where are we?

____ **a** a train
____ **b** a cruise ship
____ **c** an airplane

4 The noise was deafening from the falling pins. Where were we?

____ **a** a bowling alley
____ **b** a factory
____ **c** a sewing room

5 "These seats are so close to the field, I can see all the players," said Alex. Where was he?

____ **a** a football game
____ **b** a basketball game
____ **c** a volleyball game

6 Everyone was quietly moving from exhibit to exhibit. Where were they?

____ **a** a library
____ **b** a classroom
____ **c** a museum

7 I purchased an air pump, a filter and some ornamental snails. Where will I put them?

____ **a** in my car
____ **b** in my hot tub
____ **c** in my aquarium

Task 7

■ Read each situation. Then make a check mark in front of the correct answer.

1 I checked out a book. Where was I?

_____ **a** a classroom
_____ **b** a bookstore
_____ **c** a library

2 The surf is rough here. Where are we?

_____ **a** a swimming pool
_____ **b** an ocean
_____ **c** a lake

3 This ride is exciting! Where are we?

_____ **a** a highway
_____ **b** an amusement park
_____ **c** a racetrack

4 I better take notes. Where am I?

_____ **a** a classroom
_____ **b** an assembly
_____ **c** PE class

5 Students are busy with their experiments. Where are they?

_____ **a** a computer lab
_____ **b** a science lab
_____ **c** a blood lab

6 Everyone threw their mortarboards in the air. Who were they?

_____ **a** juniors
_____ **b** freshmen
_____ **c** seniors

7 I picked one kitten from over 100. Where was I?

_____ **a** the humane society
_____ **b** a pet store
_____ **c** a zoo

Making Inferences
Tasks Of Problem Solving – Adolescent

Task 8

■ Read each situation and determine which inference you would make. Explain your selection.

1 Kenya has many friends because she's nice to everyone. One day, her best friend saw her sitting by herself in the cafeteria, reading, even though a group of her friends was sitting at the next table. Why do you think she was sitting by herself?

  a She was studying for a test.
  b She wanted to be alone.
  c Her friends were angry with her because she wanted to sit alone.

2 The pilot came over the loud speaker and announced, "Everyone, please return to your seats and fasten your seatbelts." Why do you think the pilot made this announcement?

  a There was rough weather ahead.
  b The plane was about to land.
  c The plane was about to make an emergency landing.

3 Outback came running across the yard. There was a light snow falling, a calm breeze blowing, and the sky was overcast. As Outback reached the house, he began barking. Why do you think Outback was barking?

  a He wanted to come in the house.
  b He wanted someone to come out to play with him.
  c He was frightened by a wild animal near the house.

4 The magician put on a terrific show. When we tuned in, the audience was laughing really hard. What do you think made the audience laugh?

  a The magician made a mistake.
  b The magician cracked a joke.
  c The magician pulled a duck, instead of a rabbit, out of his hat.

5 Dean is a really handy guy. He can fix just about anything but today he's having trouble tightening a screw on the door hinge. Why do you think Dean is having trouble with such a simple task?

  a He's having trouble seeing.
  b His hands are weak from all the work he did yesterday.
  c He broke both his thumbs while driving his tractor.

6 Sue was making dinner while her mom helped Jason with his homework. When dinner was just about ready, Sue said, "Look at this spaghetti sauce. Maybe we should order in pizza for dinner." Why do you think Sue said that?

  a The sauce was burned.
  b There wasn't enough sauce for everyone.
  c The meatballs were still frozen.

■ Read each situation and think of a reason why it might have happened. Write your answer in the space provided.

1 On our trip to Mt. Kilimanjaro five years ago, the mountain was completely snow-covered. This year when we went back, the snow was almost gone. We went the same time of year each trip.

_____

2 The elk in Montana usually stay high up in the mountains. This year, they came almost all the way down to road-level.

_____

3 Our Christmas tree didn't turn brown or drop its needles this year.

_____

4 There she stood before a huge audience bowing, smiling and waving.

_____

5 The baby cried as his mother put something in the microwave and turned it on.

_____

6 Victor is a great athlete. Yesterday he came to school with a black eye.

_____

7 We were eating dinner in a restaurant. My dad cut into his steak and signaled the server to take it back to the kitchen.

_____

8 Some say, "Necessity is the mother of invention." Apply this saying to the invention of the donut hole.

_____

9 Roy was released from the hospital. He rode to the door in a wheelchair, then got up and walked to the car with his wife.

_____

10 "I must have a message," Raylene said as she looked at her phone.

_____

Expressing Consequences

A prerequisite skill to expressing consequences is determining logical outcomes or predicting consequences mentally. As students gain personal experience and learn about the experiences of others, they improve their ability to anticipate what will happen in an increasingly wide variety of situations.

As students refine their predicting skills, they also need to learn to express their predictions to others effectively. They must identify the situation or context, including the problem or anticipated event, and then describe to the reader or listener what the consequences of this event will be.

As with many other communicative interactions, the effectiveness of expressing consequences depends on the speaker's or writer's choice of language and communication style. Here are some criteria for an effective expression of consequences:

- Describe the background with appropriate detail, giving information in a logical sequence. Too much detail bores the listener. Too little information may confuse the listener.

- Highlight the problem and the choices for action to solve the problem.

- Delineate the consequences that will result from the potential action(s).

The tasks in this unit require students to summarize an everyday situation or problem with one or more logical solutions, name the solution(s), think about the logical consequence(s), and express the consequence(s) effectively.

Despite the worksheet format of these activities, work through them orally with your students as much as possible. Give them as much practice as you can to express their thoughts orally before asking them to write their responses. You can have your students work in small groups to give each one as many chances as possible to shape and express their thoughts to others. Encourage the listening students to give each speaker feedback about the clarity or effectiveness of the speaker's comments.

■ Vocabulary

It is important to understand each of these words in order to think and talk about consequences.

action	a movement; something you do
alternative	a possible choice or option to do something or solve a problem
appropriate	suitable, fitting
cause	the reason something happened; what made something happen
compromise (v)	to make adjustments in what you want in order to reach agreement with someone
consequence	what happened or would happen as a result of an action
effect (n)	a result; a consequence
effective	helpful, successful
identify	to point out or recognize something
ineffective	unhelpful, useless
issue (n)	a problem; a situation; a topic to think about
possibility	something that could happen or could be accomplished
predict	to guess what will happen or the consequence of an action
restate	to paraphrase or repeat what someone said
summarize	to repeat information briefly, keeping the main ideas and leaving out the details
visualize	to imagine how something looks or how something would happen

Task 1

■ Choose words from the box to complete these sentences correctly. Use each word only once.

alternatives	cause	consequence	predict	summarize
appropriate	compromise	identify	restate	visualize

1 A synonym for **effect** is _____.

2 Sometime when two people disagree, they can work together to reach a

_____.

3 One way to show someone you understand what the person thinks or feels is to

_____ what the person said in your own words.

4 The better you know someone, the easier it is to _____
how the person will react to a problem.

5 _____ what will happen before you do something.

6 _____ everything that happened in just one sentence.

7 What behaviors would be _____ in a library?

8 There are often several _____ to solve a problem.

9 Can you _____ the source of the noise?

10 The _____ of the false fire alarm is still under investigation.

■ Tell how the words in each pair are associated.

  1 alternative – possibility
  2 consequence – effect
  3 restate – summarize

Tracy is on the school gymnastics team. Last year, she practiced almost every day. She won first place in the final competition for both floor exercise and uneven bars.

This year, Tracy hasn't practiced as often. She has spent more time studying because her classes were harder and she wants to get into a good college.

The final competition is in two weeks, but so are Tracy's final exams. Tracy wants to do well in both the competition and the exams.

Photo courtesy of istockphoto.com © Galina Barskaya

1 Summarize Tracy's situation.

_____

_____

_____

2 What will happen if Tracy spends more time studying for her exams than she does practicing her gymnastics routines? Check the best answer.

a _____ She will do better in the gymnastics competition than on her exams.

b _____ She will not do well on either her tests or her competition.

c _____ She will do better on her exams than in her competition.

3 What will happen if Tracy spends more time practicing her gymnastics routines than she does studying for her exams? Check the best answer.

a _____ She will not do well on either her tests or her competition.

b _____ She will do better in the gymnastics competition than on her exams.

c _____ She will do better on her exams than on her competition.

Kevin's science report is due tomorrow. He has done his research and written his notes, but he hasn't written even the first draft of the report.

Kevin's parents are at a meeting tonight, so he is at home by himself. He is listening to his favorite kind of music. It's almost his bedtime and he has done nothing on his report.

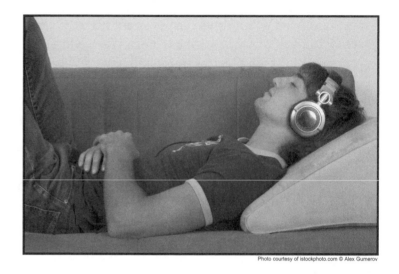

Photo courtesy of istockphoto.com © Alex Gumerov

1 Summarize Kevin's situation.

_____

_____

2 What will probably happen to Kevin's report?

_____

3 What consequences might happen if Kevin doesn't turn in his finished report on time?

_____

_____

_____

4 Should there be consequences in your classes for not turning in your assignments complete and on time? Explain your opinion.

_____

_____

_____

■ Think about each situation and predict what is likely to happen. Then express the consequences for that action.

1 Rory lives to skateboard, the faster the better. He can do all kinds of flips and tricky maneuvers. No matter how many times his parents tell him to wear a helmet, though, Rory skates without it.

Today Rory is trying a new trick. He knows it's risky, but he's not wearing his helmet.

Photo courtesy of istockphoto.com © Diane Diederich

a Predict what might happen.

_____

b What might be a consequence?

_____

2 Grace's family lives near the Gulf Coast. There is a Category 3 hurricane headed toward them. They should evacuate, but Grace's mom and dad don't want to leave.

a Predict what might happen to Grace's family during the storm.

_____

b What are some consequences that everyone from this area is likely to face because of the hurricane?

_____

_____

_____

_____

■ Think about each situation and predict what is likely to happen. Then express the consequences for that action.

Photo courtesy of istockphoto.com © Sean Locke

1 Last year, Byron brought home great report cards all year – all *As* and *Bs*. His mom was very proud of him. This year, school is harder for Byron, especially algebra. Report cards came out today and Byron got a *D* in algebra. He got an "incomplete" for language arts because he didn't turn in all of his assignments.

a Predict how Byron's mom will feel when she looks at his report card.

_____

_____

b List two possible consequences of Byron's grades on his report card.

_____

_____

2 Miranda's school just won the state championship for football. She and her friends are celebrating. One of the boys invites Miranda and her friends to ride through town in the back of his pickup truck so they can cheer and enjoy themselves. Miranda knows the driver has been drinking.

a What consequences should Miranda think about if she wants to ride in the truck?

_____

_____

b What consequences should Miranda think about if she decides not to take the ride?

_____

_____

■ You can save yourself a lot of trouble if you predict what will happen if you do something. The result of your action would be the consequence. Practice thinking about consequences by finishing these sentences.

1 If you study for your tests, then _____

_____

2 If you share a friend's secret, then _____

_____

3 If you drop out of school, then _____

_____

4 If you don't eat breakfast before school, then _____

_____

5 If you eat healthy foods and exercise, then _____

_____

6 If you copy someone else's test answers, then _____

_____

7 If you treat other people with respect, then _____

_____

8 If you make a mistake that hurts someone, then _____

_____

9 If you ignore a fire alarm in a building, then _____

_____

10 If you are caught breaking a law, then _____

_____

■ Visualize yourself facing each situation. Then tell what the consequence could be for each one.

1 You forget to charge your phone battery.

_____

2 You order more food at a restaurant than you have money to pay for.

_____

3 You don't watch a toddler you are babysitting.

_____

4 You take good care of your face and skin.

_____

5 You are surrounded by loud noise or music for hours without ear protection.

_____

6 You don't get enough sleep for days.

_____

7 You smoke at least three cigarettes a day.

_____

8 You leave your bedroom window open when you go to school. It rains that day.

_____

9 You save some of all the money you earn for your future.

_____

10 You annoy your neighbors by making noise at night.

_____

Task 5b

■ Visualize yourself facing each situation. Then tell what the consequence could be for each one.

1 You take time to plan how and when you will do your assignments.

_____

2 You promise to water a neighbor's plants while she is away, but you don't do it.

_____

3 You agree to go to a movie with a friend, but then you change your mind at the last minute.

_____

4 You drive a car without having a valid driving license.

_____

5 You notice you don't see as well as you used to, but you try to ignore it.

_____

6 You help out at home by doing chores without being asked.

_____

7 You record your assignments and appointments routinely and check your records daily to see what is scheduled to happen.

_____

8 You take music lessons but you don't practice.

_____

9 You show up half an hour late for a job interview.

_____

10 You decide what career you want before you graduate from high school.

_____

Task 6

■ Many proverbs or sayings teach us about consequences in life. Restate each saying in your own words to explain its lesson about consequences. Begin your explanation with the word IF. An example follows:

Absence makes the heart grow fonder.

If you are apart from someone you like, you will grow to like the person more than you did when you were together.

1	first come, first served	**17**	out of sight, out of mind
2	Practice makes perfect.	**18**	Many hands make light work.
3	The early bird catches the worm.	**19**	Don't put off till tomorrow what you can do today.
4	Bad news travels fast.	**20**	An apple a day keeps the doctor away.
5	Crime doesn't pay.	**21**	Do unto others as you would have them do unto you.
6	Failure teaches success.	**22**	A man is known by the company he keeps.
7	Let the buyer beware.	**23**	Ignorance of the law excuses no man.
8	Well begun is half done.	**24**	Actions speak louder than words.
9	garbage in, garbage out	**25**	April showers bring May flowers.
10	Ignorance is bliss.	**26**	As you make your bed, so must you lie in it.
11	no pain, no gain	**27**	When the cat's away, the mice will play.
12	Waste not, want not.	**28**	All work and no play makes Jack a dull fellow.
13	He who hesitates is lost.	**29**	finders keepers, losers weepers
14	Let sleeping dogs lie.	**30**	To the victor belong the spoils.
15	easier said than done	**31**	Good fences make good neighbors.
16	Look before you leap.	**32**	jack of all trades, master of none

Determining Solutions

Determining the most effective solution to a problem is a critical life skill that begins to develop in early childhood. When a problem arises, parents or caretakers are there to help their young child identify what happened and determine the best way to solve it. By adolescence, children have begun to deal with complex problems that require thoughtful solutions alone.

Most issues or problems have more than one solution, so it is important to help students brainstorm their options and evaluate the consequences of each before they decide on a solution. Adolescent students are usually good at identifying the problem, but students with thinking skill deficits often falter in determining the best solution. You may find that they:

- oversimplify the problem and its impact

- formulate a solution too quickly. Students who are impulsive will need a good measure of self-control to overcome the temptation to fix the problem fast. Help these students learn that acting before thinking can lead to solutions that are incorrect, inappropriate, illegal or dangerous.

- believe they have no alternative solutions

- disregard the experience and power of authority figures. Instead of utilizing the knowledge and experience of authority figures, adolescents often look to one another as reliable sources of information and solution finding. Unfortunately, most of their peers are inexperienced and do not have good thinking skills, so adolescents will find their advice is not always credible. Teach your students how to know when someone is credible and can be trusted.

- believe they are right without question

- believe that authority figures are right without question. Authority figures do not always offer the best solution to a problem. If you teach your students how to question authority in a positive way, they will become advocates for themselves without alienating authority figures. They will learn the art of not accepting what is read or said as the truth without investigating it further.

Determining Solutions, *continued*

In order to arrive at the best solution to a problem, students must go through the following mental processes.

First, they must understand the problem. As your students work to determine solutions for the problems in this section, help them paraphrase each problem so you know they comprehend the issue. Then ask them to identify the critical components of each problem. By doing this, your students will learn to develop solutions appropriately rather than overreact to a small problem or disregard the importance of a bigger issue.

Secondly, they must draw on past experiences to help them determine likely outcomes. Your students can learn from their mistakes and fail forward if they can apply what they have learned in previous situations to new problems. Use the activities in this section to identify the similarities and differences between problems and their solutions. This experience will improve your students' overall thinking skills as they build a repertoire of solutions that work well for them.

Finally, they must accept and reject possible solutions based on their appropriateness and correctness. Determining solutions requires students to know how to prepare or generate a set of outcomes and to choose the best result from a menu of possibilities. Having students evaluate their own arguments, beliefs, and theories is part of determining the best solution. Students should also investigate the implications and consequences of every solution prior to acting on the problem. Students who can determine the consequences of their solution will have a realistic idea of what the outcome will be and how they can handle it.

■ **Vocabulary**

It is important to understand each of these words in order to think and talk about determining solutions to problems.

advice	suggestions to someone regarding what to do about a situation
advocate (n)	a person who says something is a good idea
alienate	to make a situation go from friendly to unfriendly
alternative	a possible choice or option to do something or solve a problem
authority	a person or a group with power
belief	something you think is true; your idea or opinion
brainstorm	to let your brain think of all the new ideas or alternatives to solve a problem or do something
consequence	what happened or would happen as a result of an action
credible	capable of being believed
effective	helpful, successful
evaluate	to determine the value, worth or effectiveness of something
impulsive	acting or speaking without considering the consequences first
investigation	a careful search for facts and information
option	a choice or alternative to solve a problem or take an action
oversimplify	to make something too simple or easy
paraphrase	to restate a message in different words
result	an outcome
self-control	the ability to stay within limits you set for yourself
solution	a way to solve or answer a problem

Task 1

■ Choose words from the box to complete these sentences correctly. Use each word only once.

advocate	brainstorm	credible	option	results
authority	consequences	effective	paraphrase	self-control

1 Mr. Wilson is an _____ for adopting pets from the Humane Society.

2 Everyone ended up agreeing with Margaret because her argument was so _____.

3 One way to show someone you understand what the person thinks or feels is to

_____ what the person said in your own words.

4 The doctor spoke with Tim about the _____ of his medical tests.

5 Let's _____ some ways we can help the victims of hurricane Katrina.

6 Police officers have a position of _____ within a community.

7 Lisa wished she had thought of the _____ before she decided to skip class last Friday.

8 The jury believed that Travis was a _____ witness for the defense.

9 You have to go to the dentist today. Missing your appointment is not an _____.

10 When my friend broke my cell phone, it took a lot of _____ to keep from getting angry at her.

Task 2

■ Read the story and answer the questions.

All of the students at Clark Middle School miss Coach Day. He recently retired after coaching football at the school for 37 years. Now Clark has another football coach – Coach Kelso. Coach Kelso has a lot of new ideas, but not everyone agrees with them. He told Gary to play center instead of halfback, and Gary is very upset about it.

Photo courtesy of istockphoto.com © Suzanne Tucker

1 What is Gary's problem?

_____

2 Gary is so angry he said he will quit the team if he can't continue to play his current position.

Is this a good solution to Gary's problem? Why? _____

_____

3 Whom could Gary talk to for advice? Circle your answers and then explain why you think each one you chose is a good idea.

    a his parents   **c** his friends   **e** his brother who is a former football player

    b Coach Day   **d** his teacher   **f** his little sister

_____

_____

4 Explain the advantages and disadvantages of some other possible solutions to Gary's problem.

    a He could try out the new position and do his best.

    _____

    b He could play poorly at the new position so the coach will change his mind.

    _____

    c He could tell the coach about playing halfback before to see if he will change his mind.

    _____

    d He could find out why the coach thinks he'll do well as a center and try out the new position.

    _____

5 What do you think is the best solution to Gary's problem? Explain your answer. _____

_____

Task 3

■ Read the story and answer the questions.

Sara loves being on the soccer team. She goes to every practice and does exactly what her coach asks her to do. Her soccer skills have improved and her coach likes her attitude. As a result, he has given Sara a starting position on the team. Some of Sara's teammates are angry because they don't think she's good enough to play.

Photo courtesy of istockphoto.com © Alberto Pomares

1 Paraphrase the problem Sara has with some of her teammates.

_____

_____

2 How could Sara respond to her teammates' concerns?

_____

_____

3 Could Sara ask her coach for help? What could she say to him?

_____

4 Several teammates ganged up on Sara, telling her she'd quit if she had the team's best interest at heart. What could Sara say to those girls?

_____

5 Sara's friends want to spread rumors about the girls who ganged up on Sara. They want to post pictures and false information on the Internet. Will this help solve Sara's problem? Why?

_____

6 What might be the consequences for Sara's friends if they go through with this plan?

_____

7 What is something positive Sara's friends could do to help her with her problem?

_____

8 What do you think is the best solution to Sara's problem? Explain your answer.

_____

Task 4

■ Read the story and answer the questions.

Logan has one good friend, but that friend goes to another school. Logan spends most of his time at school by himself. Some kids tease him because he's small and takes special classes. Logan doesn't like school at all.

Photo courtesy of istockphoto.com © Jami Garrison

1 Paraphrase Logan's problem. _____

_____

2 Logan is tired of kids teasing him. He decides to spray paint their lockers, books and jackets. Is this a good way to respond to their teasing? Why?

_____

_____

3 Whom do you think would be the best person Logan could ask for advice? Circle your answer and then explain why you chose that person.

    a his good friend   **c** his teacher   **e** his stepdad
    b his school counselor   **d** his mother   **f** the principal

_____

4 Logan read about kids in other schools who became so angry they took weapons to school to hurt the bullies. Is this a good solution? Why?

_____

5 Explain the advantages and disadvantages for these possible solutions to Logan's problem.

    a He could change schools.

_____

    b He could tell the principal the names of all the kids that tease him so they can be punished.

_____

    c He could try to ignore the kids who tease him.

_____

    d He could ask the kids why they tease him.

_____

6 What do you think is the best solution to Logan's problem? Explain your answer.

_____

Task 5

■ Read the story and answer the questions.

Tim and Marc recently started a small business together. They mow lawns for several companies every Saturday. Marc arrived at the first job at 8 a.m. and started to mow. He's been mowing for over an hour and Tim still hasn't shown up.

1 What is Marc's problem? _____

2 Why might Tim be late? List as many reasons as you can.

_____

_____

Photo courtesy of istockphoto.com © Ken Hurst

3 Here are some possible solutions to Marc's problem. Explain the advantages and disadvantages of each one.

   a He could stop working and go find Tim.

_____

   b He could call Tim's home to see why he's late.

_____

   c He could quit worrying about Tim and continue mowing.

_____

   d He could call another one of his friends to help him out.

_____

4 What do you think Marc should do? Explain your answer.

_____

5 Marc and Tim have five jobs scheduled for today. What new problem will Marc have if Tim doesn't show up at all?

_____

6 What could Marc tell the business owners?

_____

7 Marc and Tim are in school during the week. How could they complete their mowing jobs?

_____

Task 6

■ Read the story and answer the questions.

Jared went to the park to play basketball with his friends. While he was there, he overheard two boys talking about vandalizing Wilson High School and hurting students. His friends think it's just a prank, but Jared is worried.

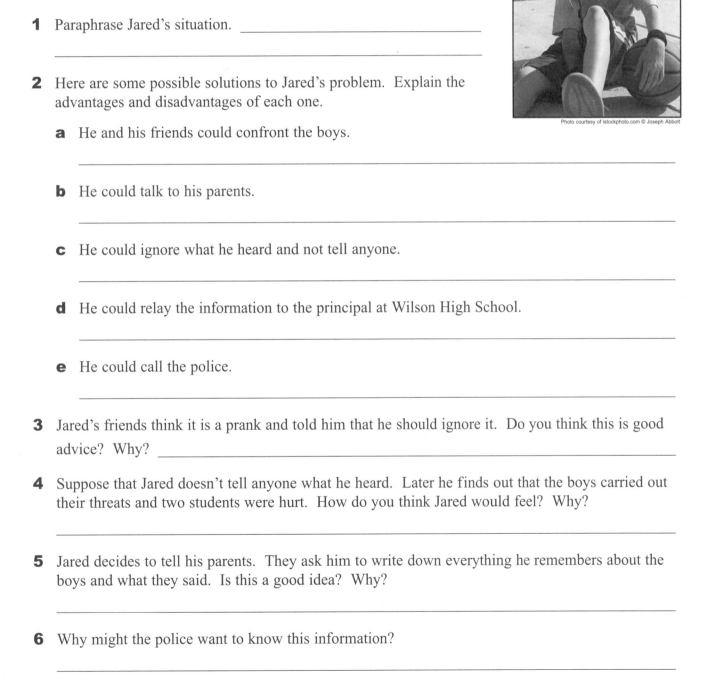

Photo courtesy of istockphoto.com © Joseph Abbott

1 Paraphrase Jared's situation. _____

_____

2 Here are some possible solutions to Jared's problem. Explain the advantages and disadvantages of each one.

  a He and his friends could confront the boys.

  _____

  b He could talk to his parents.

  _____

  c He could ignore what he heard and not tell anyone.

  _____

  d He could relay the information to the principal at Wilson High School.

  _____

  e He could call the police.

  _____

3 Jared's friends think it is a prank and told him that he should ignore it. Do you think this is good advice? Why? _____

4 Suppose that Jared doesn't tell anyone what he heard. Later he finds out that the boys carried out their threats and two students were hurt. How do you think Jared would feel? Why?

_____

5 Jared decides to tell his parents. They ask him to write down everything he remembers about the boys and what they said. Is this a good idea? Why?

_____

6 Why might the police want to know this information?

_____

■ Read the story and answer the questions.

Cal decided to visit a friend. He left home without telling his mom where he was going, and he forgot to take his cell phone with him. He's getting very tired, but he's still a long way from his friend's house.

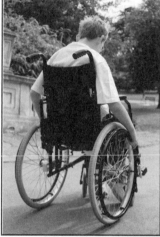

Photo courtesy of istockphoto.com © rachel dewis

1 Paraphrase Cal's problem. _____

_____

2 Cal decided to go to a friend's house, but he didn't let his mom know where he was going. Was this a good decision? Why?

_____

3 Here are some possible solutions to Cal's problem. Explain the advantages and disadvantages of each one.

a He could turn around and try to make it home.

_____

b He could ask someone for a ride.

_____

c He could use someone else's cell phone to call home.

_____

d He could ask a police officer for help.

_____

e He could rest for a while and then continue on to his friend's house.

_____

4 Suppose Cal had his cell phone with him. How would that affect his problem?

_____

5 How could Cal have avoided this situation?

_____

6 What do you think Cal will learn from this experience?

_____

Task 8

■ Read the story and answer the questions.

Sharon just got her driver's license. Her dad gave her permission to drive the family car to the mall but warned her to drive slowly and to obey the traffic laws. He told her he would take away her driving privileges if he found out she was driving recklessly. On the way to the mall, a police officer stopped Sharon. He gave her a ticket for speeding and running a red light.

Photo courtesy of istockphoto.com © Nancy Louie

1 Paraphrase Sharon's problem with the police officer.

_____

2 Paraphrase Sharon's problem with her dad.

_____

3 Why do you think Sharon ignored her dad's advice?

_____

4 Evaluate Sharon's behavior. If you were Sharon, how would you feel?

_____

5 If you were Sharon's dad, how would you feel?

_____

6 List some possible solutions to Sharon's problem with her dad. Then explain the advantages and disadvantages of each one.

_____

_____

_____

_____

7 Which solution do you think Sharon should follow? Why?

_____

Justifying Opinions

Being able to justify one's opinions is important if one is to be a credible communicator. Being a strong communicator begs one to question assumptions, question statements made by pseudo-authorities and to remain open-minded to all opinions that are supported by fact. In his seminal work in 1990, Richard Paul describes six traits of a strong thinker. All of them apply to thinkers who know the importance of being able to justify their thoughts.

1 Independence of Mind
This thinking skill can be stated as thinking for one's self. Since forming opinions requires independent thought, we need to put aside opinions we formed as children until we have proof, or justification, that those opinions are suitable. Students should be encouraged to question what is put before them as true and to reject unjustified authorities. This is especially enlightening when students are "given permission" to question what is written in accepted classroom texts.

2 Intellectual Curiosity
Intellectual curiosity is the thinking skill that is extinguished first by our society, usually at an early age. This skill requires that students find ways to explain thinking discrepancies. Using language to explain paradoxes helps to avoid deceiving oneself with easy-to-accept thoughts versus speculating about dichotomies.

3 Intellectual Courage
Courage in thinking requires that the student is brave enough to fairly address prejudice, ideas, beliefs and viewpoints no matter what strong emotions he may feel, negative or positive. In being courageous, the student can justify his beliefs by nonconformance to widely accepted opinions and ideals.

4 Intellectual Humility
Students must recognize that they don't know everything! Being naturally egocentric, they learn that they can deceive themselves when it comes to justifying opinions, so they learn to focus on the foundations of their beliefs. Acquiring intellectual humility implies a lack of pretentiousness and arrogance.

5 Intellectual Integrity
The understanding that a student needs to be true to intellectual and moral standards helps him stay true to acknowledging thinking discrepancies and inconsistencies.

6 Intellectual Perseverance
Students must not get mislead by obstacles, difficulties and frustrations that all too often happen with teens in their thinking. They must be willing to persevere even in the face of peer pressure to "follow the pack."

■ Vocabulary

It is important to understand each of these words in order to think and talk about being a good, open-minded thinker.

courage	the strength to overcome fear and face danger; bravery
curiosity	a strong desire to learn new, strange or interesting things
egocentric	being completely concerned with oneself; self-absorbed
empathy	the appreciation of what another person thinks and feels in a situation
explanation	a reason or meaning
humility	having a modest opinion of one's own importance; humbleness
independence	freedom from the control of another or others
intellect	the power of the mind to think, learn and understand; knowledge
issue (n)	a problem; a situation; a topic to think about
justify	to explain why you made a decision, took an action or formed an opinion
opinion	what you believe or feel about an issue
perseverance	insistence on a course of action or a purpose in spite of difficulties
position (n)	a way of thinking about something; point of view
situation	a condition in which you find yourself
viewpoint	a point of view; a way of thinking

Task 1

■ Choose words from the box to complete these sentences correctly. Use each word only once.

courage	egocentric	humility	intellect	opinion
curiosity	empathy	independence	justify	perseverance

1 African-American slaves gained their _____ after the Civil War.

2 You need _____ in order to think and problem-solve.

3 "Don't give up the race for class president," Dena told her friend. "You must show _____ in order to win."

4 The opposite of **fact** is _____.

5 In order to _____ your opinions, you need to present facts.

6 Many people are _____, thinking mainly of themselves rather than the feelings of others.

7 Curtis shows _____ for victims of natural disasters by volunteering to help with the cleanup and rebuilding of communities.

8 Despite all that he had achieved, the athlete showed _____ when talking to others about his many first-place accomplishments.

9 The lion in the Wizard of Oz thought he didn't have any _____.

10 "_____ killed the cat" is an expression that means "Mind your own business!"

Task 2

■ Write an **F** next to each sentence that is a fact. Write an **O** next to each sentence that is an opinion.

_____ **1** The United Parcel Service can deliver 80% of packages within the United States within 48 hours.

_____ **2** That's fast!

_____ **3** Every package is sorted and sent to Louisville, Kentucky.

_____ **4** Sending all the packages to Kentucky is a waste of time.

_____ **5** If the package needs to travel more that 200 miles, it goes by plane.

_____ **6** UPS trucks are an ugly color.

_____ **7** UPS has excellent service.

_____ **8** I'd rather send packages through the United States Postal Service.

_____ **9** In 2005, UPS delivered 3.75 billion packages and letters.

_____ **10** That's more than one package for every two people in the world.

■ Read these passages about fast food. Work with a partner to give reasons to support one side of the issue and then the other, using the statements below the passages to guide your thinking. Once you've argued both sides, state your opinion about which position you support and tell why.

1 Yay for fast food!
Fast food is convenient and tastes good. My family eats fast food about four times per week. Since there are four kids in our family, we're all going off in different directions. Fast food makes it easy for our hungry family to be fed in a hurry.

   a Tell why fast food is convenient.

   b Tell why fast food tastes good.

   c Tell why it's important to eat fast.

2 Boo to fast food!
Fast food is not good food for a healthy diet. If you eat fast food several times per week, you may start to feel sluggish. A diet filled with fresh vegetables, fruits and grains is best for the health-conscious teen.

   a Tell why fast food is not good for a healthy diet.

   b Tell why fast food may make you feel sluggish.

   c Tell why fresh fruit, vegetables, and grains are better.

My opinion:

_____

_____

_____

_____

_____

Task 4

■ Read each statement and think of reasons you might be for or against the person's viewpoint. Then use fact and opinion to give one reason that supports the person's viewpoint and one reason that argues against the person's viewpoint.

1 E-mail is the best way to communicate with people today.

For _____

Against _____

2 All adults who can't read and write at an eighth grade level should be required to attend adult classes.

For _____

Against _____

3 Children under the age of 18 who are caught smoking cigarettes should be arrested.

For _____

Against _____

4 All schools should be forced to follow a year-round calendar schedule.

For _____

Against _____

5 Since people are able to vote and enlist in the armed forces at the age of 18, they should also be allowed to drink alcohol rather than having to wait until they're 21.

For _____

Against _____

6 Identical twins should wear matching outfits from the time they're born until they start school.

For _____

Against _____

7 Working every night after school and on weekends is a good way to make money.

For _____

Against _____

8 Students who participate in a sport before or after school shouldn't have to take PE classes.

For _____

Against _____

■ Think about each situation. Then state two reasons to defend the person's position in the situation. You may use facts and opinions to justify the position.

You work at a chain restaurant and make about the same amount in tips every night. Tonight was really busy. You made twice the amount of tips you usually make. The restaurant's policy is to pool all tips and divide them among the staff – 70% goes to the wait staff, 20% goes to the kitchen staff, and 10% goes to the hostesses and busboys. Normally this is fine with you, but tonight you think it's unfair to give all of your tips to the pool. Why?

1 _____

2 _____

The person you've been dating for six months goes out with someone else. That's okay with you. Why?

1 _____

2 _____

The center on your high school basketball team is having problems with his grades. His grade point average has fallen from a B to a D in one semester. School rules are that athletes must maintain a C average at all times to play sports. You think the center should not be able to play until his grades improve to a C average. Why?

1 _____

2 _____

You're applying for a weekend job at the supermarket. The application asks, "What special skills do you bring to this position?" You say that you enjoy working with people and that you're punctual. Why are these good qualities for any job?

1 _____

2 _____

Task 5b

■ Think about each situation. Then state two reasons to defend the person's position in the situation. You may use facts and opinions to justify the position.

Some Latino girls in your school have ganged up against an African-American girl with a slight physical disability. You know this African-American girl can be rude and arrogant, but you think it's unfair for anyone to threaten anyone else. Why?

1 _____

2 _____

You're in the car with your mom when the driver of another vehicle passes her, gives her a rude gesture and then slams on the brakes. Your mom pushes on her brakes and stops just in time to avoid an accident. The driver of the other vehicles gets out and approaches your mom's side of the car. Your mom starts to get out too, but you stop her. Why?

1 _____

2 _____

For high school graduation, girls have to wear long, white dresses and carry a dozen red roses, both of which the girls must pay for. The flowers must be donated at the end of the ceremony to people in hospitals and nursing homes. You decide not to go through graduation with the rest of your classmates. Why?

1 _____

2 _____

Your fast-food restaurant job is over at 10:00 p.m. but the woman who comes to take your place on the next shift is always late. You've spoken to her about it but she's still consistently late. You decide to speak with your supervisor. Why?

1 _____

2 _____

■ Think about each situation. Then state two reasons to defend the person's position in the situation. You may use facts and opinions to justify the position.

While your family is on vacation, your neighbors install a new driveway. It is wider than their original driveway. Some of it is on your family's property. Your mom and stepdad decide not to say anything to the neighbors. Why?

1 _____

2 _____

Many schools are banning T-shirts with sayings, hats of certain colors and certain styles of dress. These rules are put in place to try to eliminate the spread of gang activity in school. You disagree with these rules. Why?

1 _____

2 _____

Today when you got to work, your supervisor reprimanded you for being rude to a customer the night before. You told her you weren't feeling well. She said that didn't matter and when you're at work, you need to be courteous and helpful. You agree. Why?

1 _____

2 _____

Your aunt has a baby whom you adore. Almost every week your aunt calls to ask if you'll stay with the baby for a few hours while she goes out with friends. She never offers to pay you but brings you gifts. You love your aunt, but you tell her that you can't watch the baby so often. You set up a schedule to watch the baby once every two months. You also tell your aunt that she'll need to pay you $5 an hour to babysit. Why?

1 _____

2 _____

Task 5d

■ Think about each situation. Then state two reasons to defend the person's position in the situation. You may use facts and opinions to justify the position.

Lots of people like chocolate. In fact, an average person consumes about ten pounds of chocolate per year! Chocolate starts out from a seed and is dried and roasted. Raw chocolate is very, very bitter, but some people have learned to like it. You only like sweetened chocolate. Why?

1 _____

2 _____

Reading is hard for you. You've been to a special reading instructor and have received tutoring. Nothing you've done has improved your reading much. Your teachers tell you that it's a matter of breaking sentences into words and words into sounds. You've done that over and over but nothing seems to help. You decide to not to go to college because of your reading difficulties. Why?

1 _____

2 _____

You deliver newspapers every morning before school. You don't mind getting up early and getting exercise by riding your bike around the neighborhood. Every morning, though, a grumpy old man yells at you to throw his paper to him right on the porch so he doesn't have to walk down the sidewalk to get it. Instead, you get off your bike and hand him the paper. Why?

1 _____

2 _____

Tanya told Sue an embarrassing story about herself. Sue promised not to tell anyone. When Tanya got to school today, though, everyone knew the story. Tanya confronts Sue, asking her for an apology. Why?

1 _____

2 _____

■ Decide whether the statements in the paragraph below each issue provide a good explanation for what happened. Tell why.

Issue   I put the magazine back in the rack next to my register.

I work at a grocery store at the check-out counter every day after school. Sometimes I get so bored, I read the magazines on the rack near my register. One day while flipping through the pages, I accidentally tore one of them.

Issue   I opposed the idea.

Our school board wants every student to do ten hours of community service every year. Students in junior high and high school could help younger students with homework. They could also work with preschool children. Others jobs might be to help at nursing homes and do yard work for the elderly. Another idea is to shop for people who can't leave their homes. The school board members said these projects would need to be done after school or on weekends.

Issue   I didn't go to the party.

My brother and I have many of the same friends, and we usually hang out together. He's 21 and I'm 19. Last weekend some guys my brother knows were having a party and they invited us. My brother said he was going to go to the party. I asked him how old the people would be there, and he said they'd mostly be 21 or older.

Issue   I wore the shirt anyway.

My little sister is babysitting to earn money. She saves every penny she makes. Last week, on my birthday, she gave me a shirt. Wow, was she ever proud of her gift to me! I didn't tell her, but I thought it was the ugliest shirt I'd ever seen.

Interpreting Perspectives

We "take a read" of other people instantly and without any conscious effort. In a flash, we form impressions of others based on personal appearance, tone of voice, what we already know about the person and our knowledge of "the way the world works." Some students mistakenly assume that the only time you need to deliberately make a good impression on someone is in a situation like a job interview, a date or some other specific context. These students need to know we all form and update our impressions of other people whenever we encounter each other.

Purposefully making an impression on someone requires thinking about how that person thinks about you or knowing the other person's perspective. The tasks in this unit will help your students understand key factors in evaluating others' perspectives.

Introduce this unit by demonstrating various emotions for your students to guess. Use your posture, gesture, facial expression and tone of voice to highlight the wealth of information we get from nonverbal cues as we observe each other.

The worksheets in this unit make excellent fodder for discussion. Use them as catalysts to help your students learn from each other as they explore the tasks together. The initial tasks familiarize students with key words dealing with perspective and demonstrate that we all make judgments about people based on what they look like, what they do and what they say. To supplement these tasks, present video clips or DVD snippets of people in various situations. Pause a few times to solicit students' impressions and predictions of what the people will say or do next. Then continue the video and allow students to check their hunches. To focus on the impressions we make just from what we hear, play just the audio of different voices and ask your students for their impressions.

Later tasks in this unit ask students to tell how people usually feel in common situations, teaching the value of learning from your own experiences and those you hear or read about. The more you know, the more likely your impressions of others will be correct.

Task 6, page 123, gives your students practice in role-playing a character, answering questions and elaborating as the character would do. Encourage constructive criticism of each role player's performance, but caution your students to be sensitive and consider the role player's perspective before they give their feedback. Teach them to criticize actions, not people themselves, and to respect different perspectives the role players demonstrate.

Interpreting Perspectives, *continued*

■ Vocabulary

It is important to understand and talk about each of these words when evaluating other people's points of view.

advice	suggestions to someone regarding what to do about a situation
analyze	to think about the parts or features of something to help you understand how it works
antisocial	preferring to be alone vs. being with others
assume	to believe something is true, even when you don't know all the facts
attitude	your way of looking at situations or how you feel about something
comfort zone	an area in which you are sure of your actions and thoughts; the physical distance a person likes to maintain without people coming any closer
constructive criticism	helpful suggestions for improvement
criteria	a rule or standard to evaluate or test something
empathy	the appreciation of what another person thinks and feels in a situation
evaluate	to determine the value, worth or effectiveness of something
feedback	a response to what someone does or says
motivate	to encourage; to give yourself or someone else a reason to do something
perspective	a person's point of view about an issue or a situation
persuade	to coax or encourage someone to do something or to change an opinion
sensitive	aware of other people's thoughts and feelings; easily hurt emotionally
viewpoint	a point of view; a way of thinking

Task 1

■ Choose words from the box to complete these sentences correctly. Use each word only once.

advice	antisocial	attitude	evaluate	motivate	persuade
analyze	assume	criteria	feedback	perspective	sensitive

1 Someone who is _____ doesn't like dances or parties.

2 What _____ should we use to judge the debate competition?

3 My brother is very _____ about his acne problem.

4 How would you _____ each singer's performance?

5 Connor hopes to _____ his dad to teach him how to drive a truck.

6 Don't _____ you know what happened until you have more information.

7 Some bosses give employees bonuses to _____ them to improve their work performance.

8 Coach Hanson gave the players specific _____ to help them boost their skills.

9 Taylor asked her older sister for _____ about what to do.

10 Students who get involved in activities at school usually have a positive _____.

11 Three detectives will _____ the evidence from the scene of the crime.

12 Personal experience or new information can change your _____ about your health.

■ Tell how the words in each pair are associated.

1 sensitive – empathy
2 perspective – viewpoint
3 assume – analyze

■ Every time people see you, they get an impression of who you are, what you think and what you might do. Each thing below influences your impression on people. Put check marks beside the ones you think matter the most. Then compare your choices with other students' choices.

1 What You Look Like
_____ what you wear
_____ the way you wear your hair
_____ your personal hygiene (neatness, cleanliness)
_____ your posture
_____ your facial expressions
_____ your eye contact (the way you look at or don't look at people)
_____ how tall you are
_____ how attractive you are
_____ your weight or body shape
_____ anything unique about your appearance

2 What You Do
_____ how you have behaved around the same people before
_____ the gestures you make, especially while you are talking
_____ the way you look and act when you are listening to someone
_____ how close you get to the people around you
_____ whether you touch the other people
_____ how you react when other people touch you

3 What You Say and How You Say It
_____ your tone of voice
_____ your expression or lack of expression
_____ what the other people already know about you
_____ what the other people guess is true about you
_____ how loudly or softly you speak
_____ how rapidly or slowly you speak
_____ the words you use (slang, dialect, formal/casual, offensive words, etc.)
_____ how much you say compared to others

4 What People Think They Know About You
_____ what experiences you have shared before
_____ what people guess about your gender, ethnicity, etc.
_____ what kind of student you are (grades, sports, activities, etc.)
_____ where you live now and/or lived before
_____ what special skills or challenges you have
_____ what your family and home life are like

■ We make assumptions about people we see, even if they are strangers in pictures. Look at each picture. Then tell at least four things you guess about each person just from the impression the person makes on you.

1

Photo courtesy of istockphoto.com © Roberta Osborne

_____

_____

_____

_____

_____

_____

_____

_____

2

_____

_____

_____

_____

_____

_____

Photo courtesy of istockphoto.com © Eileen Hart

_____

Task 3b

■ Look at each picture. Then tell at least four things you guess about each person just from the impression the person makes on you.

1

Photo courtesy of istockphoto.com © Stephanie Phillips

_____
_____
_____
_____
_____
_____

_____

2 _____
_____
_____
_____
_____
_____

Photo courtesy of istockphoto.com © Peter Hansen

_____

■ Look at each picture. Then tell at least four things you guess about each person just from the impression the person makes on you.

1

Photo courtesy of istockphoto.com © Lisa Kyle Young

_____

_____

_____

_____

_____

_____

_____

_____

_____

2

_____

_____

_____

_____

_____

_____

_____

_____

Photo courtesy of istockphoto.com © Jason Stitt

Interpreting Perspectives
Tasks Of Problem Solving – Adolescent

Copyright © 2007 LinguiSystems, Inc.

■ Look at each picture. Then tell at least four things you guess about each person just from the impression the person makes on you.

1

Photo courtesy of istockphoto.com © Shae Cardenas

_____

_____

_____

_____

_____

_____

_____

_____

2

_____

_____

_____

_____

_____

_____

_____

_____

Photo courtesy of istockphoto.com © Justin Horrocks

Task 4

■ Many people feel the same way in some situations. For example, most people are nervous when they need to speak to an audience. Tell how most people feel in each situation below.

1 get a present from a friend _____

2 about to take a test _____

3 lose $50 _____

4 late for class _____

5 physically fit _____

6 have a headache _____

7 ignored by a best friend _____

8 disappointed a parent _____

9 starting a vacation _____

10 waiting alone in a long line _____

11 computer won't work _____

12 greeted by a friend _____

13 accidentally hurt someone _____

14 can't find your cell phone _____

15 TV program interrupted by a political speech _____

16 asked to evacuate an area before a big storm _____

17 not hired for a job _____

18 good report card _____

19 get on the wrong bus or subway _____

20 receive a compliment from someone _____

■ Tell your students you will read a situation and then ask them:

How did each character feel?
What clues told you so?
When and why have you ever felt that way?

1 For the fifth time this morning, Jason asked Emma, "Why don't you want to study with me?"

2 Tricia and her stepsister were arguing again. As usual, her stepdad took her stepsister's side.

3 Marco gave the race everything he had, but he still came in third place.

4 Alex thought the third chapter in his Spanish book was even easier than the second one.

5 Yvonne wondered if she would ever have as many nice clothes as her best friend, Tory. Tory wished her family was as much fun to be around as Yvonne's family.

6 Martin thought he would mess up during his recital, but his piano teacher told him, "Martin, that was the best you've ever played that piece. It was perfect!"

7 The track meet had been postponed due to rain for the sixth day in a row. Tom wondered if he could run as fast on a damp track once the rain stopped.

8 Becca's mom was already 45 minutes late picking her up. If her mom was stuck in traffic another 20 minutes, Becca would be late for her babysitting job.

9 Todd was deep in thought as he walked through the hall. He bumped right into Ana and knocked down her books. She blushed as he helped her pick up her books.

10 Kate and Dan brought their science projects to class and set them on the counter. Dan did his on the computer and it looked professional. Kate did hers by hand and some of the ink was smudged.

11 As usual, Daryl smiled as the tests were returned. Mark sighed. He didn't even turn his test over to see his grade when the teacher put it on his desk.

12 Nancy never had to worry about her diet before. Now that she had diabetes, she and her mom were in a class to learn how to stay healthy even with this condition.

13 Chad clamped his hands over his ears. His parents were fighting again and he didn't want to hear what they were saying.

Cut the boxes apart. Give each student the description of a person to portray. The students may designate an actual person who fits the role or may role-play a general character fitting the role. Have a student introduce himself in character. The student should then stay in character to answer questions from the group, elaborating as the character might. Then ask the group to evaluate each role player's performance in terms of normal expectations for that character.

President of the U.S.	accountant	school bus driver
principal	teacher	school nurse
librarian	adolescent	guidance counselor
politician campaigning	astronaut	news reporter
hair stylist	homemaker	detective
rock star	nutritionist	musician
movie star	fast-food server	Olympic athlete
senior citizen	dentist	sports coach
police officer	party guest	movie character
sports athlete	party host	video game character

Transferring Insights

Transferring insights to new contexts is the ability to learn from past experiences and apply that knowledge to new situations. It's a thinking skill we use every day and, for most of us, the ability to draw from past experiences is automatic. Our brain's memory is triggered by the new experience, and skills we've successfully used in the past to solve problems are quickly engaged again in the new scenario. We can control our impulsivity and frustration if we're not able to solve the problem quickly. We actively search for similarities from our past. We're able to mull things over and engage our brain to systematically go through the thinking steps.

This level of competence is not what we find for many students with language and cognitive disabilities. The evidence for this is in the number of times you find yourself saying, "This is just like the assignment we did yesterday" or "Remember what you did the last time we had this situation?" The good news is that our students' abilities to transfer insights to new contexts will get better if we engage them in the appropriate training and then follow-up by giving them sufficient practice to master the skill.

This chapter focuses on leading students through a series of questions they can learn to ask themselves whenever they encounter a new situation. You'll find a mix of question types for each situation and no right or wrong answers. This section is meant to bring all of the question-asking and cognitive skills together. Use the questions as a guide. You are the expert with your students. You understand and know the school, community and home environments. If necessary, rephrase questions so they're relevant to your students' environments.

As Dr. Art Costa (1991) so thoughtfully reminds us, it is our mission to develop in our students a "new form of intellect – a global intellect, with people who know how to live in rational, humane, peaceful, and compassionate relations with each other and the environment."

Our students need to thrive in a global economy that is multicultural and multilingual. It is important to expose them to a wide variety of experiences and to help them use those experiences to develop their thinking and problem-solving skills. As they get older, students need to have a well-developed repertoire of successes and failures from which to draw on as they tackle new experiences and solve new problems. Our goal is to help them develop the skills they need to learn from their mistakes so they will make fewer mistakes in the future. Teaching students to transfer thinking skills to new contexts is one step toward the achievement of this goal.

Thinking is hard work, but with the proper instruction, it is our hope that your students' thought processes will improve. We hope your students begin to apply skills across many situations, produce them with more spontaneity, and become more accurate thinkers and problem solvers.

■ Vocabulary

It is important to understand each of these words in order to think about past experiences, learn from them and apply that knowledge to new situations or problems.

automatic   happening on its own, without a person controlling it

competence   being adequately qualified; capable

compromise (v)   to make adjustments in what you want in order to reach agreement with someone

context   the facts or circumstances that surround a situation or event

encounter (v)   to come upon or meet with

engage   to participate in an activity

experiences   actions you have taken or things that have happened to you

failure   an act that results in not achieving the desired results; lack of success

frustration   a strong feeling of dissatisfaction caused by unresolved problems

impulsive   acting or speaking without considering the consequences first

mull   to think about carefully

scenario   an imagined or possible sequence of events

similarities   ways things or ideas are alike

society   human beings as a group; all people

spontaneous   happening without any apparent reason

success   the achievement of a goal

systematic   based on a well-organized, thorough, step-by-step plan

Task 1

■ Choose words from the box to complete these sentences correctly. Use each word only once.

competence	experiences	impulsive	scenario	spontaneous
encounter	frustration	mull	similarities	success

1 The coach was pleased with the _____ of the team.

2 Although some of the rules are different, there are many _____ between women's softball and men's baseball.

3 Lawson made an _____ decision to walk home with his friend after school instead of riding the bus.

4 Kristi will need to _____ over the information about each college before deciding which one to attend next year.

5 You can use your past _____ to help you make decisions about what to do in new situations.

6 One possible _____ involves working weekends to help pay for the trip.

7 It is normal to have a feeling of _____ when others tease or criticize you.

8 We were so sure of Sophia's _____ in math that we voted her class treasurer.

9 The news report said there was a _____ explosion at the factory last night.

10 When you _____ a new problem, it's a good idea to brainstorm several solutions.

■ Compare the meanings of the words in each pair.

1 success – failure
2 impulsive – systematic
3 automatic – spontaneous

■ Read the story and answer the questions.

Photo courtesy of istockphoto.com © George M Muresan

Winter in many parts of the country means snow and getting to do great activities outside. It also means protecting your skin. Today Jody and Mia are enjoying a snow vacation day from school. The deep snow is perfect for packing, and the girls are determined to make the world's tallest snowman.

1 How should you protect your skin during cold winter weather?

_____

2 How should you protect your skin during warmer summer weather?

_____

3 What is important to remember about the sun's rays and snow or water?

_____

4 What's right about the way the girls are dressed?

_____

5 The sky is grey and it's snowing heavily in this picture. What do you know about sun protection that applies to this type of weather?

_____

6 Several years ago Mia got frostbite on her fingers. What should she do differently when she's outside in cold weather so this doesn't happen again?

_____

7 Besides your skin, what other parts of your body need sun protection?

_____

8 Have you had a problem with sun protection? If so, what worked well? What would you do differently?

_____

Task 3

■ Read the story and answer the questions.

Troy wasn't feeling well and went to the doctor. His doctor prescribed some medication that Troy must take twice a day for ten days. When Troy's mom picked up the prescription, the pharmacist told her of some possible side effects that Troy might have. He also warned her that Troy should stay out of the sun while taking the medication. If he doesn't follow this warning, the medicine won't work.

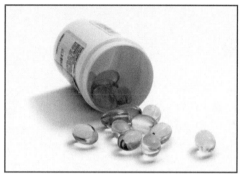
Photo courtesy of istockphoto.com © Don Bayley

1 Tell how prescription medicines and non-prescription medicines are alike and how they're different.

Alike _____

Different _____

2 Troy has football practice every day after school. Why might this be a problem?

_____

3 Troy felt well five days after he got the medication, so he stopped taking it so he could go to the beach. Why is this a problem?

_____

4 If Troy were your friend, what would you say to him about his decision to stop taking the medication?

_____

5 Why would the doctor prescribe medication for ten days if Troy felt well after taking it for only five days?

_____

6 Have you had a problem like this? If so, what worked well? What would you do differently?

_____

Task 4

■ Read the story and answer the questions.

Sonia bought this jacket with money she earned babysitting. Her friend Tina asked to borrow it and Sonia agreed. When Tina returned the jacket, the pocket was torn and the sleeve was stained. Sonia wants Tina to buy her a new jacket, but Tina says it was an accident. She fell when the pocket got caught on a railing. She says that if you lend someone an item, you should expect accidents to happen. She's unwilling to replace the jacket.

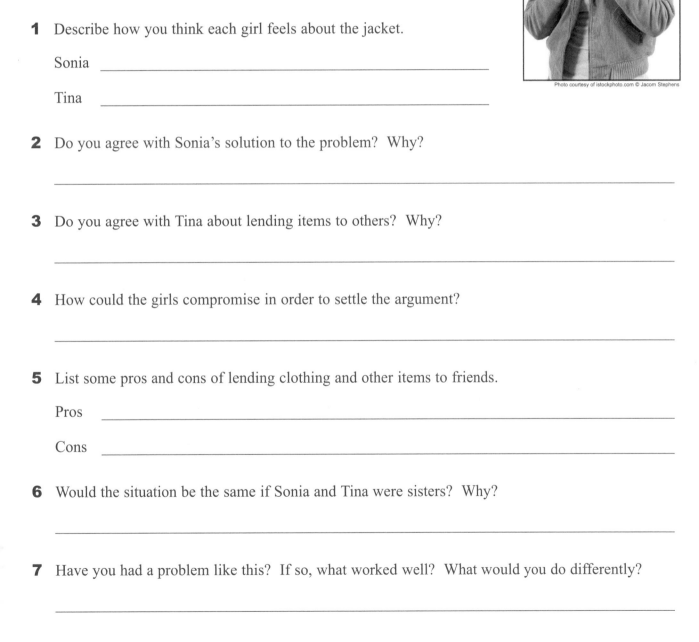

Photo courtesy of istockphoto.com © Jacom Stephens

1 Describe how you think each girl feels about the jacket.

Sonia _____

Tina _____

2 Do you agree with Sonia's solution to the problem? Why?

_____

3 Do you agree with Tina about lending items to others? Why?

_____

4 How could the girls compromise in order to settle the argument?

_____

5 List some pros and cons of lending clothing and other items to friends.

Pros _____

Cons _____

6 Would the situation be the same if Sonia and Tina were sisters? Why?

_____

7 Have you had a problem like this? If so, what worked well? What would you do differently?

_____

Task 5

■ Read the story and answer the questions.

Photo courtesy of istockphoto.com © Galina Barskaya

Alena looks confident on the outside, but she's not on the inside. She's new to her school and doesn't know very many people yet. She also feels awkward and uneasy around guys she likes, and so she's nervous about dating. The first school dance of the year is in a few weeks. It's a "girl's choice dance" where the girls invite the guys. Alena wants to go, but she's afraid to ask anyone to go with her.

1 What is Alena's problem?

_____

2 How could Alena overcome her nervousness enough to ask someone to the dance?

_____

3 Some guys told Alena that Davante would like her to ask him to the dance. How might this be a problem?

_____

4 What if Alena finds out the guys aren't telling her the truth about Davante? How could she react to this rumor?

_____

5 Alena decides to ask Antonio to the dance. What might happen?

_____

6 If you were Alena's friend, what could you say to help boost her confidence?

_____

7 Have you had a problem like this? If so, what worked well? What would you do differently?

_____

Task 6

■ Read the story and answer the questions.

Trevor is taking a summer band class. Today Trevor's band instructor called and cancelled class, so Trevor went to his friend's house instead. When Trevor's mom got home from work, she was worried because she didn't know where he was. Last time Trevor's plans changed and he didn't call, his mom made him promise that he'd let her know where he was from now on. Now he's grounded for a whole week!

Photo courtesy of istockphoto.com © James Pauls

1 Why do you think Trevor's mom wants him to call her whenever his plans change?

_____

2 As children get older, do you think their parents should continue to worry about them? Why?

_____

3 Trevor thought this situation was different because he was at a friend's house. What's wrong with Trevor's thinking?

_____

4 Trevor is so upset with his mom that he told her he wants to move in with his dad. Is this a good solution? Why?

_____

5 What can Trevor do to prove to his mom that he's trustworthy again?

_____

6 Trevor often forgets to turn in his school assignments on time and bring home the school newsletter each month. How are these issues similar to what happened today?

_____

7 Have you had a problem like this? If so, what worked well? What would you do differently?

_____

Task 7

■ Read the story and answer the questions.

Laureen is a star player on her school's basketball team. Last night her team played against their biggest rivals from Woodridge Middle School which is two hours away. Laureen played a great game and her team won, and they celebrated on the bus the whole way home. Today's another story, though. She has an important chapter test in science. She meant to study for the test last night on the bus, but it was too noisy. When she got home at 11:00 p.m., she was too tired.

1 Do you think that school sports teams should be allowed to play away games on weeknights? Why?

_____

2 Laureen thinks that school athletes should have an extra day to study for tests when they have a weeknight game. Is this a good idea? Why?

_____

3 Do you think Laureen will do well on the science test? Why?

_____

4 How do you think Laureen's teacher would react if Laureen explained the situation and asked to take the test another day?

_____

5 What could Laureen do differently the next time she has a test the day after a game to be better prepared?

_____

6 Have you had a problem like this? If so, what worked well? What would you do differently?

_____

■ Read the story and answer the questions.

Photo courtesy of istockphoto.com © Henry Chaplin

Jasmine knows about the harmful effects of smoking cigarettes. Even so, she started smoking because she believes it will help her lose weight and stay slim. Yesterday her dad found a lighter in her jeans pocket when he was doing the laundry. When he started questioning her, Jasmine told him to mind his own business. She said that she could quit any time she wanted.

1 What are some of the health risks associated with smoking?

_____

2 Do you agree that people who smoke can quit any time they want? Why?

_____

3 Jasmine's dad gave her some information that said it's a myth that smoking helps people lose weight. He offered to cook healthy meals at night and take walks with her after work. Is this a good solution? Why?

_____

4 What effect might Jasmine's smoking have on her relationship with her friends?

_____

5 Last weekend Jasmine's friends invited her to a movie, but she didn't have the money to go. What connection could there be between Jasmine's smoking and her lack of money?

_____

6 If you were Jasmine's friend, what advice would you give to her about this issue?

_____

7 Have you had a problem like this? If so, what worked well? What would you do differently?

_____

Integrating Thinking Skills

This unit presents diverse realistic situations for your students to explore and respond to, using the strong thinking skills they have now developed via earlier units. Each situation includes a photo and a brief description of the context of a specific situation. The problem is not always apparent from the photo, so students will need to use their past experiences, common sense and fund of general information to infer more background information.

The situations with questions are generally arranged in a hierarchy of complexity, both for the particular situation and for the thinking/language needed to consider each question thoughtfully and then express an appropriate response.

These situations and questions work well for individual work, small group discussion or whole class presentation. Whether working with individual students or groups of students, add your own observations and opinions to the general discussion. Encourage flexible thinking and different personal or cultural perspectives. For example, in response to the question *What are good ways to travel safely by subway?*, students might give these and other responses:

- Never travel by yourself.
- Make sure you know exactly where you're going.
- Don't talk to anyone.
- Don't use the restroom unless someone is with you.
- Take a cell phone.
- Don't draw attention to yourself.
- Don't hang around the platform long.
- Don't even use a subway. Take a bus or walk instead.

To enrich your students' learning, some of the later situations in this unit offer ways for your students to delve beneath the surface of an issue by consulting resources. Otherwise, many of the questions make excellent written tasks, particularly after your students have discussed the situation and their various responses to the questions.

Finally, once your students are familiar with the format in this unit, ask them to work independently or in small groups to select pictures and generate interesting questions about a hypothesized situation, complete with appropriate responses.

Kim is happier moving around than sitting in a chair. When she does her homework, she often lies on the floor. She changes her position often. Sometimes she does yoga poses while she reads or thinks about a school assignment.

1 Why do some people dislike having to sit in a chair for long periods of time?

2 What are some situations that require people to stay seated for a long time?

3 Why do some people mind sitting for a long time more than other people?

4 What are some benefits of being physically active?

5 What are some risks of being physically active?

6 In what position or positions do you prefer to read? Why?

7 In what position or positions do you prefer to use a computer keyboard? Why?

8 In what position or positions do you prefer to use a handheld computer? Why?

9 Kim does yoga for exercise. What kind of exercise do you like best? Why?

Toby takes the subway to and from school every day.

1 What might be the reason Toby takes the subway instead of walking?

2 What might be the reason Toby takes the subway instead of a bus?

3 What information do you need to know in order to ride a subway?

4 How could you find out which train to take and when to be on the platform?

5 How do subway passengers know when to get off the subway?

6 What are some potential risks of riding a subway? Explain why each one is risky or what could happen.

7 What are good ways to travel safely by subway?

8 If you board the wrong subway train, what should you do?

9 If a subway is crowded, which passengers should be given priority for getting seats? Explain why.

These girls are celebrating Ilana's birthday at an amusement park.

1 Which girl is Ilana? How do you know?

2 Why do you think Ilana wanted to have her party at an amusement park?

3 Some of the guests want to ride the wildest rides, but others don't want to. How could the group make sure they don't lose each other in the crowd?

4 What did each guest need to think about before coming to this party?

5 Each guest brought a present for Ilana. What should happen with the presents while the guests go on rides?

6 The party was scheduled for 2:00–5:00 in the afternoon. It's now 5:15 and the guests want to stay longer to go on more rides. What should these kids think about now?

7 How do you think the guests' parents will react if their kids stay at the park until 7:00? Why?

8 Who should make the decision about whether to stay longer or leave on time? Why?

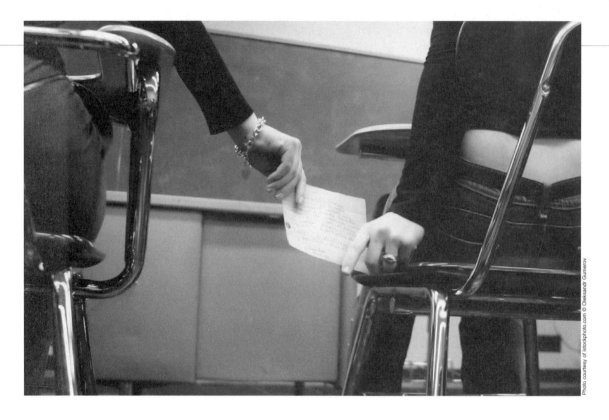

Across the nation, there has been an alarming increase in cheating. Some students blame the poor examples set by adults. Others blame the increased pressure for good grades to get into college.

1 Give three example of ways students might cheat on schoolwork or tests.

2 Whose responsibility is it to make sure students don't cheat on tests? Explain why.

3 Does cheating hurt anyone? Explain your rationale.

4 Compare cheating on a classroom test to plagiarizing a report by copying from an Internet or a library source. Are they equally wrong? Explain your rationale.

5 How do you think your teachers view cheating in class?

6 Why don't all students cheat or plagiarize?

7 Explain why there is more cheating in schools today than there was 25 years ago.

8 What would be a just consequence for a student who cheats on a test? Explain why that consequence would be fair.

9 If you observe students cheating, what should you do about it? Justify your opinion.

Mike and his sister, Julie, don't get along well. Julie thinks Mike should do more to help with cleaning up after meals and keeping their home neat. Mike has a headache from Julie's constant nagging.

1 What does "constant nagging" mean?

2 What might make it hard for Mike to just ignore Julie?

3 Julie nags Mike. What is a better way to persuade her brother to help out around the home?

4 Julie's mom thinks girls are responsible to keep things in order in the home. Is that fair? Explain your answer.

5 What could Mike do to stop Julie's nagging?

6 Why do some brothers and sisters get along better with each other than others?

7 What are some good ways Mike could reduce his stress level when he's around his sister?

8 If you were Mike and Julie's parent, what would you say or do to help your kids get along better?

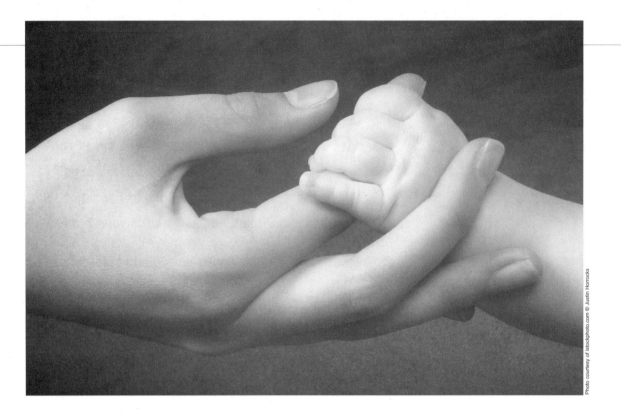

Melanie is 16 and lives with her parents. Her mom just had a baby girl named Cora.

1 What does this picture make you think and feel? Explain why.

2 Why are infants so helpless?

3 How will Melanie's life at home change when Cora comes home from the hospital?

4 How might Melanie feel about her baby sister? Explain why.

5 Melanie's parents expect that she will help take care of Cora. Do you think that's fair? Explain your opinion.

6 What kinds of things could Melanie do to help her mom at home?

7 What should Melanie do if she thinks her parents are taking advantage of her by asking her to be so involved with Cora?

8 Melanie's parents spend a lot of time with Cora now. How could they reassure Melanie that they love her as much as ever now that Cora is part of the family?

9 How can having such a young sister help Melanie?

It's prom night. Rory and Tina have been a couple for two years and they have looked forward to senior prom together for months. In July, Rory will leave town for a long time. He will enter the military to become a marine. Tina will have a part-time job while she goes to a local junior college.

1 Tell the clues in this picture that suggest this is a scene from a prom night.

2 What does it mean to be a couple in high school?

3 How do you think this couple feels in the picture? Explain your answer.

4 Why do you think Rory wants to become a marine?

5 What should Tina think about when she looks for a part-time job for next year?

6 Rory and Tina hope to get married someday, but they know it is too soon right now. How can they keep up their relationship once they are far away from each other?

7 What advice would you give to this couple to help them stay together?

The seniors at Edison High School are having a class picnic in a park. The whole class was divided into teams to play some games.

1 What kind of activity are they doing in this picture? Tell what makes you think so.

2 What do you think would be the best way to divide a whole class into teams? Explain your reasoning.

3 Some students have physical disabilities. How could the teachers and students make sure that all students can participate in the activities in some way?

4 What are some good activities for a class picnic like this? Tell why the activities would work well in this situation.

5 It's a very hot day and the students are mostly in the sun. What should they do to protect themselves from the sun's rays?

6 Do you think having a class picnic is as important as spending the same time learning? Justify your opinion.

7 What do the teachers need to think about during the class picnic? Why?

8 This class has almost 300 students. How can the teachers keep track of the students to make sure they are safe and no one wanders off on their own?

9 There are other people using the park besides this class. What should the students think about to respect the other park visitors?

Tamara was adopted as a baby through a legal adoption service. Her parents told her she was adopted when she was five years old. She lives with her parents and a younger sister, who was not adopted.

1 What can you tell from this picture about the relationship between Tamara and her mom?

2 Why do you think Tamara's parents adopted her?

3 What did Tamara's parents need to think about before they adopted her?

4 Now that Tamara is 16, she wants to learn more about her birth mother and possibly her natural father. Why do you think she wants that information?

5 How do you think Tamara's birth mother would feel if Tamara contacted her?

6 How do you think Tamara's parents feel about her wish to learn more about her birth mother and possibly her father?

Marco's father is laid off and his mother has a minimum-wage job. There are eight people in his family. Marco wants to get a part-time job.

1 What is a "minimum-wage job"?

2 What kinds of jobs are usually paid the minimum-wage rate? Why?

3 What are some logical reasons Marco wants a part-time job?

4 What should Marco think about as he decides what job to seek?

5 How could Marco find out what jobs are available?

6 What should Marco think about before he has a job interview?

7 Until now, Marco has taken care of his younger brothers and sisters after school. What are some other ways these children might be cared for while Marco works?

8 How could Marco's job interfere with doing his homework?

9 How could having a part-time job help Marco besides earning money?

Elly and Pam are students at Wilson Middle School. They use the Internet for homework assignments and to chat with friends.

1 Compare using the Internet to using the library to do homework assignments.

2 What other resources can students use to do homework assignments?

3 Why do many students use the Internet rather than the phone to talk with their friends?

4 Elly's parents put locks on some Internet sites. They told Elly she can only use the Internet when one parent is at home. Why do you think they made that rule?

5 What can students do to stay safe while communicating with friends on the Internet?

6 What information is important for students and children to know about online chat groups?

7 What are the potential risks of communicating with a stranger on the Internet?

Ben and Lian are cousins. Ben moved to the United States six years ago and quickly became fluent in English. Lian just moved to the U.S. She is struggling with the English language and is constantly pestering Ben to help her. Ben needs to study and wants to spend time alone with his friends, but Lian is always around.

1 Ben was studying in the park when Lian interrupted him. What could Ben say to Lian?

2 Despite being frustrated with Lian, Ben helped her with her English. Why do you think Ben helped Lian?

3 Ben's mom insists that he help Lian learn English after school, which is usually when Ben hangs out with his friends. How could Ben compromise with his mom?

4 Lian wants to hang out with Ben and his friends. Ben's friends say Lian is loud and immature. What could Ben say to his friends?

5 What are some reasons Lian acts immature?

6 Lian knows she bugs Ben a lot. What could she do so Ben has time for himself and for her?

Last year the Bay City school district cut the soccer programs at all grade schools. For a while it looked as though the Dolphins would never play another soccer game. Then some high school students picked up the ball. They volunteered to be coaches, and, with help from the players and their parents, they raised enough money to buy uniforms and equipment. Now the Dolphins are state champions!

1 Which of these is the most logical reason that the soccer program was eliminated? Explain why the other reasons aren't logical.

    a There weren't enough students to make a team.

    b School budgets were cut.

    c The coaches quit.

    d The players didn't like their uniforms.

2 What does the expression *picked up the ball* mean?

3 What are some reasons high school students would volunteer as coaches?

4 What are some things the players could have done to raise money for their team?

5 Some schools cut athletic and fine arts programs to save money. Is this a good idea? Why?

6 How could schools keep programs going?

Lisa and Ellen are using math skills to design furniture. Their teacher, Ms. Hanson, wanted to spice up her classes, so she showed her students how to use math to design a chair. The students determined things like the chair's dimensions, weight and cost to build. When they were finished with their design, Ms. Hanson had a local woodworker build the chair. The idea took off! The students loved this project so much, they wanted to design more furniture.

1 What does *spice up* mean?

2 Why do you think Ms. Hanson wanted to spice up her classes?

3 What does the sentence *The idea took off!* mean?

4 Why do you think the students loved this project?

5 How do you think the principal felt about Ms Hanson's furniture design project?

6 Why would Ms. Hanson ask a woodworker to build the chair?

7 Some teachers think students are spending too much time on furniture design and not enough time on other subjects. What could they say to Ms. Hanson?

We all need to take care of the environment. One day each September is designated International Coastal Cleanup Day. On that day, people from all over the world work to clean coastal areas. This year, workers at the Shedd Aquarium in Chicago took part in this event. They cleaned up a beach with the help of some local students. The group picked up over 154 pounds of trash.

1 What would happen if no one cleaned up trash in our cities?

2 Chicago is a large city. What problems would a large city have if no one collected trash for several days?

3 Lots of trash is buried in landfills. Land is becoming scarce. What are some ways people can reduce the amount of trash that goes to landfills?

4 The workers and volunteers who cleaned the Chicago beaches picked up more than 2,700 cigarette butts and over 500 food wrappers. What could visitors to the beaches do?

5 What might you do if you went to a beach on vacation and it was littered?

6 What might happen to litter if it's left on the beach?

7 What are other ways to protect the environment?

8 Many cities along freshwater lakes use the water for homes. What might happen to the water quality if there were no checks on pollution?

Some parents take their children's sporting events too seriously. They shout at the coaches, heckle the officials and get upset when their children make mistakes. One coach decided that the parents of his players were too angry. He told them that they could not talk at all during the games. If they did, a police officer would escort them to their cars and they would have to leave the park.

1 What might be reasons parents become so angry at their children's games?

2 Why would the coach tell the parents they could not talk at all?

3 What good things could parents say at a game?

4 Some players were embarrassed because their parents got so angry. What would you say to your parents if they embarrassed you that way?

5 Some parents want to cheer for their players and the team. How could they cheer and still obey the no-talking rule?

6 If you were a player, would you like the fans to be quiet during your game? Why?

States that have graduated driver's license programs for teens are pleased with these programs. Teen drivers in these states get fewer tickets. They are also involved in fewer crashes. Best of all, fewer teens are killed in car accidents. These programs increase privileges as students get older as long as they maintain good driving records.

1 What problems do adolescent drivers have that older drivers do not have?

2 You are sixteen and you think you should be able to get your driver's license. Your parents disagree. They say you have to be eighteen. Is waiting a good idea? Why?

3 States with graduated programs restrict the number and age of passengers in a car driven by a teenager. Is this a good restriction? Why?

4 States with curfew laws have severe consequences for teens caught driving after curfew. What might be a good reason for teens to be allowed to drive after curfew?

5 Your friend wants a ride home but you are not allowed to drive with passengers in the car. What can you say to your friend?

6 Your parents said that almost 6,000 teens are killed in car accidents each year. They don't want you to drive to school. How could you persuade them to let you drive to school?

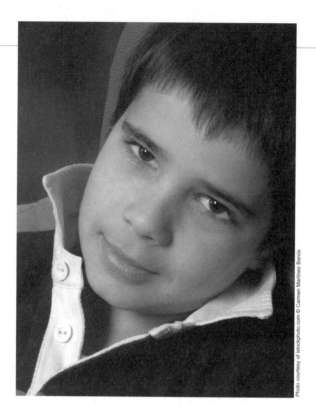

The Hernandez family recently emigrated from Mexico. Now they live next door to Juan and his family. Juan's parents speak to them in Spanish and English. Juan doesn't know Spanish, and he has a hard time understanding Mr. and Mrs. Hernandez's English. Juan's parents are pestering Juan to learn Spanish, but he doesn't want to. Juan's parents want him to change his mind, so they have started to speak only Spanish at home.

1 What does *emigrate* mean?

2 How do you think Juan's parents learned Spanish?

3 How might the Hernandez family have learned English?

4 Why does Juan have a hard time understanding the Hernandez's English?

5 How do you think Juan feels about his parents' decision to speak only Spanish at home?

6 How might you convince Juan to learn Spanish?

7 How could Juan help the Hernandez family?

8 Do you think it's a good idea to learn a second language? Why?

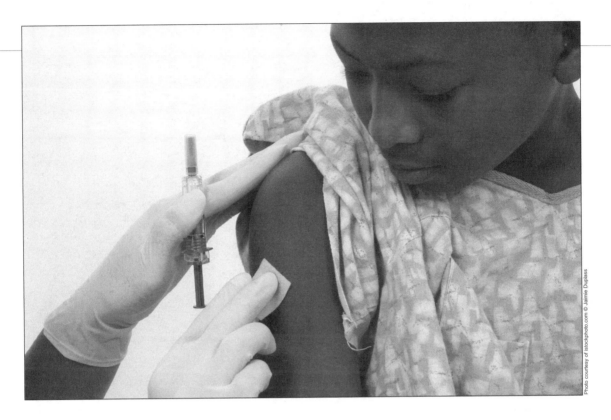

Recently there was a flood in the town where Shayla lives. Flood waters can carry a disease called *tetanus*, which can make you very sick. It can get into your body through small cuts or sores. The doctors in Shayla's town suggested that all residents get a shot to protect them from this dangerous disease.

1 Why did doctors recommend getting a tetanus shot?

2 You only need to get a tetanus shot once every 10 years. How do you know if you might need one?

3 Some people do not want the shot. Is it a good idea to refuse it? Why?

4 There may never have been an outbreak of disease in your city, but how could a flood change that?

5 How can people prepare for emergency situations like a flood?

6 Some homeowners refused to evacuate their homes. They wanted to protect their belongings. Is this a good idea? Why?

7 When dangerous weather is expected, TV and radio stations send out many storm warnings. How do think these warnings help people?

8 How might things change in a city after the floodwaters are gone?

Renee got straight A's in grade school, but she had a secret. She couldn't read. Renee fooled her teachers and parents by finding unique ways to learn. This year Renee is in the sixth grade at Crest Middle School, and her new teachers have discovered her secret. Now she's going to special classes for students with learning disabilities.

1 Why do you think Renee kept her secret for so long?

2 How do you think her parents felt when they learned Renee could not read?

3 How do you think Renee felt when her secret got out?

4 Renee is embarrassed about her learning disability. What could you say to boost her confidence?

5 If you were one of Renee's teachers, how would you feel about being fooled by one of your students?

6 If her reading disability had been discovered earlier, how might school have been different for Renee?

7 Do you think a student with a learning disability can go on to college? Why?

8 Some kids tease Renee about going to special education classes. What could Renee do when they tease her? What could she say to them?

9 Renee's parents suggested she ignore kids who tease her. Is that hard to do? Why?

This couple is having an argument about money. The young man needs to save his money for college. He doesn't like to spend money going to the movies. His girlfriend thinks he doesn't want to go out because she isn't pretty. She also thinks he's being cheap because he doesn't want to spend any of his money on her. Staying home and watching a video or TV just isn't on her list of exciting things to do.

1 Which person seems to be more concerned about money?

2 Tell one good thing about not spending money on a movie.

3 Tell one good thing about going out every now and then.

4 Why does the girl think her boyfriend doesn't think she's pretty enough to meet his friends?

5 What should the girlfriend do? Explain your answer.

6 What is a good compromise for this couple? Explain your answer.

7 These two people have different opinions about what makes a great weekend activity. Read these opinions and guess which ones were said by the boy and which ones were said by the girl. Then tell why each opinion is reasonable.

  a "Staying at your house to watch TV all the time gets boring."

  b "Movies are so expensive . . . and then there are the snacks."

  c "I like to get dressed up to go out."

  d "Sometimes I like to go hang out with our friends."

  e "I like staying at home and having friends over to hang out."

8 Read about these compromises and guess which of these people said each one. Tell why you thought so.

  a "If we go out one night a month, will that make you happier?"

  b "If we go out two nights a month, will you be able to afford that?"

  c "If we want to go out any time, would you agree to each of us paying our own way?"

  d "When we go out, let's look for free activities to attend."

9 Choose the characteristics that best describe the boyfriend.

  a worried about having enough money for college

  b worried about pleasing his girlfriend

  c worried about his friends not wanting to hang at his house

  d worried about his parents getting tired of having him home

10 Choose the characteristics that best describe the girlfriend.

  a likes to stay home and watch TV with her boyfriend

  b likes to rent movies to watch at home

  c likes to go out and socialize with friends

  d likes to get dressed up to go to dinner and a movie

11 Assume the position of a judge. It is your job to help this couple reach a good decision about dating that they both will follow and enjoy. Decide what questions you'll ask each one. Then tell how you'll come up with a solution.

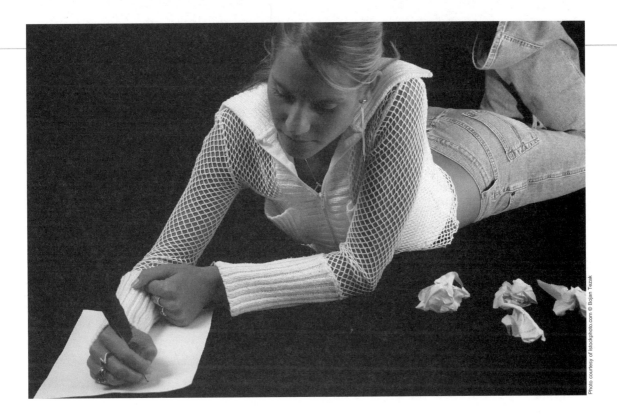

Sonja has a problem. One of her friends just left for college. His college is 100 miles away, so she writes emails to him often. Her other friend is attending trade school in electronics. He lives at home and sees Sonja a few times a month. Sonja's problem is that she likes both boys but the boys don't like each other. She thinks that if one finds out she's seeing the other, they'll get into a fight. Then she might lose both friends. She feels like she's being disloyal to both of them, but neither friend asked her not to date anyone else.

1 What is the major problem Sonja has?

2 Would the situation change if both boys lived in Sonja's town? Explain your answer.

3 Next year, Sonja will go to college in a different city. Will that change the way she feels about her two friends? Explain your answer.

4 Why does it matter to Sonja that the two boys don't like each other?

5 Do you think the boy who is away at college suspects that Sonja has a boyfriend at home? Explain your answer.

6 Do you think the boy who lives in Sonja's area suspects she likes the boy at college? How do you know?

7 Sonja thinks she should tell each boy about the other and explain to each that she values each one's friendship. She'll say that it really doesn't matter that the boys don't like each other because they never have to be together. What do you think about Sonja's plan?

8 The boy at college is serious and studious. The boy at home is curious and outgoing. Make a list of other characteristics each boy might have based on what you know already. Then explain your thoughts.

9 Sonja loves to learn and is an adventurous girl who will try anything once. Make two lists of characteristics you think Sonja may need to get along with both boys. Then explain your ideas.

10 When Sonja writes emails to each boy, she uses different styles for each. Below is a list of words. Put a check mark by the way you think Sonja writes to the boy in college. Put a plus sign by the way you think she writes to the boy at technical college. Then explain each decision you made.

_____ **a** poetic

_____ **b** humorous

_____ **c** factual

_____ **d** descriptive

11 If you are a girl, imagine you are Sonja. Write a short note to each boy about your feelings. If you are a boy, write two short notes to Sonja about your feelings. Share your notes with your teacher.

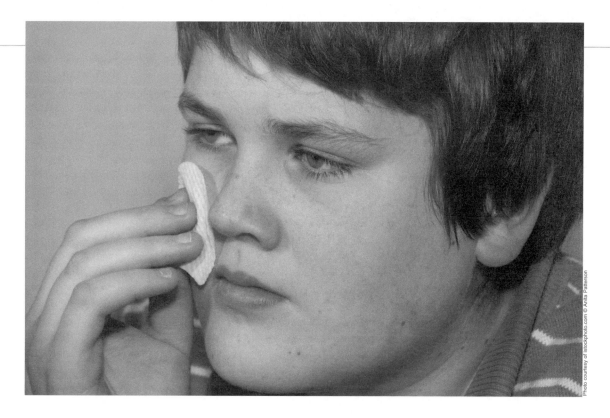

Jay just turned 15 and he's never had acne problems until now. His dad told him how to care for his skin. Some of Jay's friends also have acne, but Jay feels that his is the worst. He doesn't want to hang out with other kids like he used to. Talking with girls has gotten harder, too. Some of his friends are beginning to tease him, not about his acne but about the fact that he wants to be left alone. Jay likes staying home when his face breaks out, but he's willing to go out with his friends when his skin is clearer.

1 Pick which sequence you think is correct for Jay's skin care routine.

    a dry, wash, rinse   **c** wash, rinse, dry
    b rinse, wash, dry   **d** wash, dry, rinse

2 What problems might Jay be creating by staying home when his face breaks out?

3 According to what you know about acne, which of these foods may cause acne?

    a French fries   **e** a and c
    b bananas   **f** b and d
    c chocolate   **g** none of the above
    d yogurt

4 According to what you know about hygiene, which one of these habits encourages clear skin?

  a taking vitamins

  b scrubbing your face with a washcloth

  c washing your face at least three times per day

  d using an antibacterial soap

  e c and d

  f a and b

  g none of the above

5 Read each issue below. Tell how each student feels about Jay's acne. Explain your answers.

  a Martha is one of Jay's best friends. She thinks she can help him feel better about his acne by telling him about her treatments from the dermatologist.

  b Jeremiah is Jay's older friend. He has acne but he doesn't care. He thinks Jay should just forget about it.

  c Bruce doesn't have acne but he has one leg shorter than the other, which makes it difficult for him to play sports. He thinks Jay is lucky to just have acne and not have a physical challenge.

  d Karla only breaks out at certain times. Otherwise, her skin is clear. She tells Jay that he'll eventually grow out of his acne problems.

6 Below are some adult opinions of teen problems. Choose one you think best shows how adults should be with teens. Support your opinion.

  a Jay's mom wants to spend money on a dermatologist. She believes the doctor will be successful in helping Jay improve his skin.

  b Jay's dad remembers his acne and tells Jay to do the best he can to keep his skin clean. He tells Jay not to spend money going to a dermatologist because he'll eventually outgrow the problem.

  c Jay's school counselor has Jay read several handouts about the care and treatment of healthy skin.

7 Choose an opinion below and give reasons to support the opinion. Acne is:

  a not much of a problem since most teens get it at some time.

  b a moderate problem that can cause some embarrassment

  c a big problem because of the way people react to it.

8 Do research about teenage acne. Summarize your findings by writing a short, one-page paper about its cause and cure.

Keisha and Gran are very close. That's partly because Gran has raised Keisha since she was an infant. Another factor is that Gran has always taught Keisha to set goals for herself and work to achieve them. Now that Keisha is one year from graduating high school, she's asking Gran for her advice about college and careers. She admits she's nervous and unsure about going to college. She worries about failing.

Gran knows that Keisha is bright and that she works hard. She also knows that Keisha is shy and not very willing to take risks. Gran tells her that nothing worthwhile ever came easily. Keisha looks at Gran with respect and love. She knows that Gran is right, and she promises herself that she will succeed.

1 How does Gran know that Keisha is bright?

2 How does Gran know that Keisha is a hard worker?

3 Why do you think Gran raised Keisha?

4 Think of two ways to describe what kind of a person Gran is.

5 How do you think Gran and Keisha will pay for college? Consider these options and tell the pros and cons of each.

   a While she's still in high school, Keisha gives up her position on the school newspaper to start working after school and on weekends.

   b After graduation, Keisha gets a full-time job for a few years and saves for college.

   c Keisha applies for a full-ride scholarship to the college of her choice.

   d Keisha goes to a community college for two years. Then she transfers to a four-year college to finish getting her degree.

   e Keisha takes out student loans.

   f Keisha gets a job in the evenings and on weekends.

   g Gran works a second job to pay for college.

   h Keisha goes to trade school in cosmetology rather than attend college.

6 Which of these options do you think is the best? Explain your answer.

7 How might this saying apply to Keisha? *If at first you don't succeed, try, try again.*

8 Keisha's high school has college counselors on staff. What are some questions Keisha could ask her counselor about college that might ease her fears?

9 Keisha is interested in creative writing. She's also a very good organizer. Which of the careers below would be best suited to her skills? Why?

   a cosmetology

   b engineering

   c newspaper reporter

   d teacher

   e screenplay writer

   f fashion designer

   g chef

   h editor

10 How can Keisha apply what she has learned from Gran to her life in college? Consider things that Gran probably told Keisha as she was growing up about working hard, taking responsibility for her actions, and how to treat others.

Lonely Baloney is a rock band. Five friends started the group when they began taking band in fourth grade. Now that the guys are juniors in high school, their sound is pretty good and they play lots of gigs.

When people first see Lonely Baloney, they think the guys play heavy metal or hip-hop. Most people are surprised to find out that they play everything from the Big Band Era to New Age music. This kind of variety gets them more gigs than they can play.

Now Lonely Baloney needs to make a decision. Two of the band's members are going to college next year. Two other members are joining other bands. The leader singer is going solo. The band has about $15,000 in the bank that the guys have earned from their gigs, and they're not sure what to do with it.

1 Pretend you are a music writer for *The Rolling Stone*. What are some questions you might ask Lonely Baloney?

2 Why do people think the band would play heavy metal or hip-hop?

3 What is music from the Big Band Era like?

4 What does New Age music sound like?

5 How do musicians sound when they are first learning to play their instruments? Why?

6 What is a *gig*?

7 Below is some additional information about each band member. Based on this information, tell who you think should get the band's money. Explain your reason.

 a The two band members who are going to college have music scholarships.

 b The two that are joining other bands live at home.

 c The one member who is going solo needs to move to Los Angeles.

8 If you said "All of them" in the question above, you might be right. Can you think of a reason why four of the members might lend the money to the member going solo?

9 If the band members lend the money to the guy going solo, how long do you think he should have to pay back the other members?

10 How do you think he'll get the money to pay them back?

11 How do you think the band came up with its name?

12 Do you think it's a good name for a band? Why?

Glossary

accuracy	correctness
accurate	correct, on target
action	a movement; something you do
adapt	to change something to make it work for you
advice	suggestions to someone regarding what to do about a situation
advocate (n)	a person who says something is a good idea
alienate	to make a situation go from friendly to unfriendly
alternative	a possible choice or option to do something or solve a problem
analyze	to think about the parts or features of something to help you understand how it works
angles	different ways to analyze a task or a problem
antisocial	preferring to be alone vs. being with others
apply	to use
appropriate	suitable, fitting
assess	to take a close look at something and analyze it
assume	to believe something is true, even when you don't know all the facts
assumption	information you believe to be true without any evidence
attitude	your way of looking at situations or how you feel about something
attribute (n)	an inherent characteristic or quality of something
authority	a person or a group with power
automatic	happening on its own, without a person controlling it
behavior	what you do, your actions

belief	something you think is true; your idea or opinion
brainstorm	to let your brain think of all the new ideas or alternatives to solve a problem or do something
category	a distinct group or class to which objects or concepts belong
cause	the reason something happened; what made something happen
characteristic	a specific quality that distinguishes or identifies one person, thing or class from another
choice	something you choose; an option
chronological	arranged in order by time
clarify	to explain or make something clear/understandable
classify	to organize things into groups
cognizance	knowledge; awareness
comfort zone	an area in which you are sure of your actions and thoughts; the physical distance a person likes to maintain without people coming any closer
compare	to examine two things and determine how they are alike
competence	being adequately qualified; capable
composition	what an object is made of
compromise (v)	to make adjustments in what you want in order to reach agreement with someone
concerned	caring about what happens
conclude	to reach a decision after thinking something through; to finish
conclusion	a final judgment after you have considered all the evidence and ideas
consensus	an agreement among a group of people
consequence	what happened or would happen as a result of an action

consider	to examine; to think about
constructive criticism	helpful suggestions for improvement
context	the facts or circumstances that surround a situation or event
contrast	to pick out differences between and among people, places, things or ideas
cooperate	to work well with someone
courage	the strength to overcome fear and face danger; bravery
creativity	the ability to use your brain to think of new ideas or ways to do things
credible	capable of being believed
criteria	a rule or standard to evaluate or test something
curiosity	a strong desire to learn new, strange or interesting things
current situation	what is happening now
decide	to take a position after deliberation
deduce	to reason about cause and effect
describe	to represent something in words; to paint a mental picture
detect	to notice or discover something; to identify
differences	ways things or ideas are unlike
differentiate	to distinguish between two things
dilemma	a problem with no easy solution
disagreement	two or more people having different opinions about the same issue
disloyal	unfaithful to a person or a cause
distinguish	to perceive a difference between and among people, places, things or ideas
divided	disagreeing with each other

drawback	a disadvantage about a situation or a solution to a problem
effect (n)	a result; a consequence
effective	helpful, successful
efficiency	effectiveness
egocentric	being completely concerned with oneself; self-absorbed
elaborate (v)	to expand upon what someone says
empathy	the appreciation of what another person thinks and feels in a situation
encounter (v)	to come upon or meet with
engage	to participate in an activity
environment	everything around you
evaluate	to determine the value, worth or effectiveness of something
evaluation	a critical examination of something to see if it meets the criteria
evidence	facts, proof
execution	the carrying out of a plan of action
experiences	actions you have taken or things that have happened to you
explain	to describe how or why something works or is true
explanation	a reason or meaning
express	to communicate your beliefs, opinions and knowledge
failure	an act that results in not achieving the desired results; lack of success
feedback	a response to what someone does or says
flexible	willing and able to change your thoughts and attitudes, to adopt
form an opinion	to decide your view or attitude about an issue

frustration	a strong feeling of dissatisfaction caused by unresolved problems
function	what an object does or is used for
generalize	to learn something and then apply it to similar situations or ideas
humility	having a modest opinion of one's own importance; humbleness
hypotheses	a thoughtful guess or theory about an idea or behavior you want to test
identify	to point out or recognize something
imagine	to form a picture in your mind, to pretend or daydream
imply	to make a deduction
impulsive	acting or speaking without considering the consequences first
inappropriate	not correct, unacceptable
independence	freedom from the control of another or others
ineffective	unhelpful, useless
infer	to draw a conclusion based on what you see or hear
inflexible	unwilling to adapt your thoughts based on new or additional information
intellect	the power of the mind to think, learn and understand; knowledge
investigate	to search for evidence, causes, or information
investigation	a careful search for facts and information
irrelevant	not important for a certain purpose; unrelated; beside the point
issue (n)	a problem; a situation; a topic to think about
justify	to explain why you made a decision, took an action or formed an opinion
language	a communication system shared by a group
logical	sensible

mediator	a neutral person who listens to both sides and renders a decision to resolve a conflict
memorize	to rehearse something well enough to remember it without any help
merit	to have worth or value
modify	to change a plan, idea, or solution
monitor	to keep track of progress or actions
motivate	to encourage; to give yourself or someone else a reason to do something
mull	to think about carefully
objectives	actions to take to achieve a specific goal
observe	to watch carefully; to notice
open-minded	flexible, willing to consider new ideas or opinions
opinion	what you believe or feel about an issue
option	a choice or alternative to solve a problem or take an action
organize	to arrange things thoughtfully and logically
original	novel, creative, not copied or imitated
outline (n)	a list of the main points of an article, a report or a lecture
oversimplify	to make something too simple or easy
paraphrase	to restate a message in different words
perseverance	insistence on a course of action or a purpose in spite of difficulties
perspective	a person's point of view about an issue or a situation
persuade	to coax or encourage someone to do something or to change an opinion
plan (n)	sequenced steps to follow to achieve a goal

position (n)	a way of thinking about something; point of view
possibility	something that could happen or could be accomplished
precise	exact
predict	to guess what will happen or the consequence of an action
preference	something you prefer over other choices
prioritize	to sequence things according to their importance or need for immediate attention
problem	a challenge to solve
reason (n)	why something happened; a cause
reason (v)	to think logically and coherently
relevant	relating to what is being discussed or considered; pertinent
resources	tools to provide information or assistance for a project or a problem
restate	to paraphrase or repeat what someone said
result	an outcome
role model	someone you respect and would like to emulate
scenario	an imagined or possible sequence of events
self-control	the ability to stay within limits you set for yourself
sensitive	aware of other people's thoughts and feelings; easily hurt emotionally
separate (v)	to make a distinction between and among people, places, things or ideas
sequence (v)	to arrange things in a logical order
similarities	ways things or ideas are alike
situation	a condition in which you find yourself

society	human beings as a group; all people
solution	a way to solve or answer a problem
spontaneous	happening without any apparent reason
strategy	a plan to complete an objective, a job, or a plan of action
success	the achievement of a goal
summarize	to repeat information briefly, keeping the main ideas and leaving out the details
suspicion	a feeling or guess that something is a problem, someone did something or something happened
systematic	based on a well-organized, thorough, step-by-step plan
thinking patterns	habits in ways of thinking about things or ideas
thought	an idea
urgent	needing immediate action or attention
viewpoint	a point of view; a way of thinking
visualize	to imagine how something looks or how something would happen

Correct answers are provided for several of the tasks. Suggested answers are given for other tasks, except for those items that have a wide variety of appropriate, acceptable responses. No answers have been provided for those items because the answers will vary based on students' personal experiences, perspectives, etc. Be sure to ask students to explain their answers using logical thinking to enrich expressive language skills as well as to gain insight into answers that differ from those listed here. Use your best clinical judgment to accept all reasonable answers that are supported by logical thinking as correct.

■ Sequencing

page 15

1. chronological
2. reason
3. original
4. opinion
5. logical
6. modify
7. sequence
8. plan
9. justify
10. organize

1. Both deal with the future, neither is certain to happen.
2. When you prioritize, you sequence things by importance.
3. One way to organize things is to classify them into groups.
4. You give a reason to justify your opinion or action.

page 16

1. a. 5
   b. 4
   c. 3
   d. 2
   e. 7
   f. 6
   g. 1

2. a. 3
   b. 2
   c. 5
   d. 1
   e. 6
   f. 4

3. a. 5
   b. 3
   c. 2
   d. 4
   e. 6
   f. 1

4. a. 5
   b. 2
   c. 8
   d. 1
   e. 6
   f. 4
   g. 3
   h. 7

page 18

1. a. 3
   b. 2
   c. 1

2. a. 1
   b. 3
   c. 2

3. a. 2
   b. 1
   c. 3

4. a. 2
   b. 1
   c. 3

5. a. 2
   b. 3
   c. 1

6. a. 3
   b. 1
   c. 2

7. a. 3
   b. 1
   c. 2

8. a. 3
   b. 2
   c. 1

9. a. 2
   b. 3
   c. 1

10. a. 3
    b. 2
    c. 1

page 19

1. a. 2
   b. 3
   c. 1
   d. 5
   e. 4

2. a. 6
   b. 1
   c. 2
   d. 4
   e. 3
   f. 5

3. a. 4
   b. 2
   c. 1
   d. 3
   e. 5
4. a. 3
   b. 1
   c. 4
   d. 2
   e. 5
   f. 6
   g. 7
5. a. 3
   b. 2
   c. 5
   d. 1
   e. 4

page 20

1. a. 5
   b. 3
   c. 7
   d. 2
   e. 1
   f. 4
   g. 6
2. a. 4
   b. 3
   c. 2
   d. 5
   e. 1

page 21

1. c
2. c
3. b

page 22

1. c
2. a
3. d

page 23

1. a. 5
   b. 3
   c. 1
   d. 4
   e. 2
2. c

page 24
Answers will vary.

■ Asking and Answering Questions

page 28

1. precise
2. proper
3. option
4. explain
5. standards
6. expand
7. hasty
8. improper
9. unproductive
10. reasonable

pages 33-34

1. b, c, f
2. a, b, d
3. b, c, d

page 35

1. b
2. a
3. b, d, e
4. d

■ Comparing and Contrasting

page 38

1. analyze
2. disagreement

3. compare
4. mediator
5. function
6. compromise
7. relevant
8. difference
9. distinguish
10. characteristics
11. divided
12. describe

page 39
Answers will vary.

page 40

1. wrench
   screwdriver
2. helmet
   shin guards
3. stethoscope
   mallet
4. blood pressure cuff
   tongue depressor
5. lobster
   clam
6. St. Bernard
   border collie
7. statue
   instrument
8. liberty
   Christianity
9. making music
   typing
10. sweeping the floor
    brushing teeth

page 41

6 They rode something.
4 She was playing a game; he was trying to keep a secret.
9 She went water-skiing; he went snow skiing.

5 They assigned homework.

7 She carried personal items; he carried school items.

10 They ate something.

5 He teaches math; she teaches history.

9 They went skiing.

8 They bought something.

1 They went to get haircuts.

3 They wanted privacy.

10 She ate fish; he ate beef.

1 They went to different places.

3 He was in the bedroom; she was in the living room.

6 He rode something motorized; she pedaled.

8 He bought something to drink; she bought something to eat.

2 They enrolled in school.

4 They hid something.

2 He is a young boy; she is a teenager.

7 They carried something.

page 42

1. sun
2. gases
3. photos
4. air waves
5. water is close to the shore
6. water is away from the shore
7. Antarctic
8. Arctic
9. United States
10. Argentina
11. moon
12. earth

page 43

1. darkness
2. light
3. where to migrate
4. pay attention to impulses
5. Venus
6. Pluto
7. falling stars
8. dirty snowballs
9. oval
10. disk with arms

page 44

1. Pollution is caused by the Earth's rotation.
2. Wetlands are named for lands that have swimming pools.
3. Automobiles cause soil pollution.
4. Electricity is more polluting that gasoline.
5. An ecosystem is made up of only plants and animals.
6. Ecosystems can be destroyed by animals.
7. Herbivores eat soil.
8. Grasslands cannot be restored after damage.
9. Coral reefs cannot be damaged by SCUBA divers.
10. Farmers rotate crops to relieve boredom.
11. Most animals use tools.
12. Man is the only animal that communicates.

pages 45-46
Answers will vary.

■ Identifying Problems

page 49

1. evidence
2. problem
3. consider
4. urgent
5. drawback
6. issues
7. paraphrase
8. cause
9. suspicion
10. dilemma
11. describe
12. elaborate

1. Both mean to make something clear.
2. Both mean to retell what someone else said/wrote. Restate implies saying the same thing again. Paraphrase implies using your own choice of words to summarize or restate what was said/written.
3. A suspicion is a guess that's not based on proof. Evidence is proof.
4. Both a problem and a dilemma are things to solve. A problem can have pleasant and/or unpleasant choices; in a dilemma, the choices are equally unpleasant.

page 50

1. poor grades; a D in U.S. History
2. car smashed; anyone hurt?; tree now on top of car; getting car repaired/replaced; cost of cleaning up; insurance issues

page 51

1. woman washing floor, someone walking where she's scrubbing; woman annoyed by walker's lack of care/concern
2. woman slipping on high-heeled shoe; might sprain her ankle; heel stuck in sidewalk crack

page 52

1. knee brace on knee; person can't be as active as normal; need to consider what clothing fits over brace; may be uncomfortable; if on a team sport, may be off the team for a while
2. front right bumper fell off; probably in an accident; anyone injured?; insurance issues, repair costs/time, car in drivable condition?; cause of accident/ liability issues

page 53

1. not familiar with feel/touch of a computer keyboard; may not have typed in years; may have arthritis; may have vision difficulties with computer screen
2. bike rider flipped off bike; might be hurt; might need transportation to get medical attention; getting bike home if rider injured

page 54

1. wanted to swim but no lifeguards; could be too dangerous to swim; need to find beach with lifeguard on duty
2. sunburn might hurt/become uncomfortable; might need soothing lotion/gel; might be dehydrated

page 55

1. a. missing his appointment
   b. kids need supervision/care until parent returns; not old enough to be left alone
   c. Answers will vary.
2. a. wants to eat whatever he wants; not hungry for fruit

b. missed classes; grades have slipped
c. poor diet, lack of exercise, health condition

page 56

1. wants good grade on project but can't get boys to cooperate; doesn't like being teased about appearance
2. the dog ran away; finding the dog
3. finding another place to play ball
4. can't be with your friends because your dad wants you with him at the same time
5. different idea about what "clean room" means between her and her mom
6. can't concentrate on homework because of the noise; doesn't have another place to study where it's quiet

page 57

1. a. Mandy doesn't suffer anymore. Adele loses Mandy right away; she feels guilty.
   b. Adele can be with Mandy awhile longer. It will be painful to watch Mandy suffer in pain.

2. a. He would do okay on the math test but get a 0 on his language arts report.
    b. He will avoid a 0 for the report, but he won't do well on the math test.
    c. He will not do very well in either subject.
    d. done his report earlier so he would have time to study for the math test

■ Detecting Key Information

page 60

1. outline
2. evidence
3. current
4. detect
5. analyze
6. summarize
7. issue
8. prioritize
9. irrelevant
10. organize

page 62

1. It rained today.
2. Tracy sits next to me in Spanish.
3. Chad's stepmom bakes really good cookies.
4. We had a great track team last year.
5. It's already 3:00.
6. I'm so hungry!
7. Have you seen my book bag?
8. I hate the smell of glue.
9. It's almost time to go home.
10. What's that noise?
11. I think I'm getting a cold.
12. I heard about Steph and Dave.

page 63

Identify these sentences:
1. 1, 2
2. 1, 3
3. 1, 3
4. 1, 3
5. 1, 2
6. 1, 2
7. 2, 3
8. 1, 3
9. 2, 3
10. 1, 3

page 64

1. Some pizzas are spicier than others.
   Most pizzas are round but some are square.
2. Some people prefer plain buns, but I prefer poppy-seed buns.
   You need to be hungry to eat one of these.
3. Some plants need watering more often than others.
   Ivy is one of the hardiest house plants.
4. Do you do your own laundry?
   Our washer takes about 25 minutes to do one load.

page 65

1. Carla, broke her leg, skating
2. picnic, starts at 11:00 a.m., we can go at noon
3. one ticket, $5, 10 for $40
4. no cavities, checkup, need to brush my teeth more carefully
5. usually take the bus, museum, today we're driving, bring a stroller
6. Grandma's favorite, sweater, hole, from moths
7. need a pencil, math test
8. Candidate Nelson, cut taxes, increase the minimum wage, cure cancer
9. ordered a gift for Grandpa online, put a bow on the package
10. good weather, dog, dig holes, lot next door
11. Derek got a rash on his face from his new glasses

page 66

2. The detective was an eye witness that Diana carried something out of the store.
3. It shows that Diana wouldn't want to wear the sweaters herself.
5. Her mother trusted her to use her charge card.
6. Diana might have wanted to resell the sweaters on the Internet.

7 It's evidence that she bought the sweaters.

8 It's evidence that Diana was doing a favor for her mother by buying the sweaters.

page 67

Sunday; over 300 people; Pine Run; 37th annual Pine Run Ham Radio Amateur Club Flea Market; Shoppers and traders; from all over New England; Bert Graff; organized the event; success; fewer people; Our group will die out without more young folks

The government depends on ham operators to help when the Internet is down; Hurricane Katrina brought down communication towers in 2005, ham operators were a key source of communication

Pine Run event included computers and other modern electronic devices to draw more young people

It's easy to be a ham operator; take a test; get a license with your own call letters; Clark plans to campaign at local high schools next year; to recruit some young ham operators

page 68

1. best friends with Sharon for eight years
One month ago, Sharon started dating Roy; spends all her time with him; I'm lost without her; get my best friend back again

2. I buy whatever I want, not whatever I need; decent allowance; earn some money; I buy things I don't need; Will I always be this way; I have no clue how I can stop this ugly habit

3. I've always done well in sports; I quit basketball this year; My parents and my coach keep telling me they are disappointed; I want to try other activities; How can I persuade my parents and teachers to let me make my own choices

■ Making Inferences

page 71

1. differentiate
2. similarity
3. observe
4. imply
5. express
6. situation
7. reasoned
8. explain
9. concluded
10. decide

1. You use reasoning to make an inference.

2. Both involve communicating with others either to tell how or why something works or is true or to share your beliefs, opinions and knowledge.

3. You use both to make decisions about what happened or will happen and why.

4. Both involve making a decision about something after careful thought.

page 72

1. b
2. a
3. c
4. b
5. b
6. c
7. a

page 73

1. b
2. a
3. b
4. c
5. c
6. c
7. b

page 74

1. a
2. b
3. c
4. a
5. b
6. a
7. b

page 75

1. a
2. c
3. b
4. c
5. b
6. b
7. a

page 76

1. b
2. a
3. b
4. a
5. a
6. c
7. c

page 77

1. c
2. b
3. b
4. a
5. b
6. c
7. a

pages 78-79
Answers will vary.

■ Expressing Consequences

page 82

1. consequence
2. compromise
3. restate
4. predict
5. visualize
6. summarize
7. appropriate
8. alternatives
9. identify
10. cause

1. An alternative is one of several possibilities.
2. Both are tied to a cause and are the result of what happened or would happen.
3. Both involve repeating information; summarizing is brief and only includes the main points while restating includes the details.

page 83

1. Tracy has been spending more time studying than practicing gymnastics this year because she wants to get into a good college. The final competition and Tracy's final exams are in two weeks, and she wants to do well in both of them.
2. c
3. b

page 84

1. Kevin has a science report due tomorrow. He's started it but it's not finished, and it's almost his bedtime. Instead of working on it, he's at home listening to music.
2. He will turn it in late.
3. He will get a lower grade; he will get in trouble.
4. Answers will vary.

page 85

1. a. He might have an accident.
   b. He might get a head injury.
2. a. They might get trapped or hurt.
   b. houses and businesses could get damaged; electricity could go out; there will be a lot of cleanup

page 86

1. a. angry, concerned, disappointed
   b. Byron might get grounded or lose privileges.
2. a. the driver may be drunk; her parents will get mad; she might get hurt
   b. what her friends will think; whether she should call the police about the driver

pages 87-90
Answers will vary.

■ Determining Solutions

page 94

1. advocate
2. effective
3. paraphrase
4. results
5. brainstorm
6. authority
7. consequences
8. credible
9. option
10. self-control

page 95

1. The new football coach wants Gary to play a different position than he's been playing.

Answers will vary for remaining items.

page 96

1. They don't think she deserves a starting position on the team.

Answers will vary for remaining items.

page 97

1. He doesn't like school because he doesn't have any friends and kids tease him.

Answers will vary for remaining items.

page 98

1. His business partner is over an hour late for work.

Answers will vary for remaining items.

page 99

1. He overheard some kids talking about doing something bad and he doesn't know what to do.

Answers will vary for remaining items.

page 100

1. Cal didn't tell anyone where he was going or bring a cell phone, and he's too tired to make it to his friend's house.

Answers will vary for remaining items.

page 101

1. She's getting a ticket for speeding and running a red light.
2. She didn't listen to her dad about driving carefully.

Answers will vary for remaining items.

■ Justifying Opinions

page 104

1. independence
2. intellect
3. perseverance
4. opinion
5. justify
6. egocentric
7. empathy
8. humility
9. courage
10. Curiosity

page 105

1. F
2. O
3. F
4. O
5. F
6. O
7. O
8. O
9. F
10. F

pages 106-112
Answers will vary.

■ Interpreting Perspectives

page 115

1. antisocial
2. criteria
3. sensitive
4. evaluate
5. persuade
6. assume
7. motivate
8. feedback
9. advice
10. attitude
11. analyze
12. perspective

1. A sensitive person has empathy toward others.
2. Both relate to how a person sees something.
3. Analyzing implies careful thought; assuming does not.

pages 116-122
Answers will vary.

■ Transferring Insights

page 126

1. success
2. similarities
3. impulsive
4. mull
5. experiences
6. scenario

7. frustration
8. competence
9. spontaneous
10. encounter

1. Success is the achievement of a goal; failure is a lack of success.
2. Impulsive acts are done without thinking; systematic thinking is step-by-step and thorough.
3. Spontaneous events happen without an apparent reason; things that are automatic happen on their own but usually have reasons.

pages 127-133
Answers will vary.

■ **Integrating Thinking Skills**

pages 135-164
Answers will vary.

References

Armbruster, B.B., Lehr, F., & Osborn, J. (2001). *Put reading first: The research building blocks for teaching children to read—kindergarten through third grade.* Washington, D.C.: The Partnership for Reading.

Armstrong, T. (2003). *The multiple intelligences of reading and writing.* Alexandria, VA: Association for Supervision and Curriculum Development.

Bowers, L., Huisingh, R., & LoGiudice, C. (2005). *TOPS 3: elementary.* East Moline, IL: LinguiSystems, Inc.

Bowers, L., Huisingh, R., LoGiudice, C., & Orman, J. (2003). *No glamour language & reasoning.* East Moline, IL: LinguiSystems, Inc.

Bowers, L., Huisingh, R., LoGiudice, C., Johnson, P., & Orman, J. (2005). *Spotlight on reading comprehension: Making inferences and drawing conclusions.* East Moline, IL: LinguiSystems, Inc.

Costa, A. (Ed.). (1991). *Developing minds: A resource book for teaching thinking (3rd ed.).* Alexandria, VA: Association for Supervision and Curriculum Development.

Costa, A.L. (1991). *Teaching for intelligent behavior: Outstanding strategies for strengthening your students' thinking skills* (Workshop resource handbook). Bellevue, WA: Bureau of Educational Research.

Cotton, K. (1991). Close-Up #11: Teaching Thinking Skills. Retrieved July 14, 2000, from Northwest Regional Educational Laboratory's School Improvement Research Series Web site: http://www.nwrel.org/scpd/sirs/6/cu11.html

Davis, K.C. (2001). *Don't know much about planet earth.* New York: Harper Collins Publishers.

Elder, L., & Paul, R. (June 1996). Universal Intellectual Standards. Retrieved from The Critical Thinking Community Web site: http://www.criticalthinking.org/resources/articles/universal-intellectual-standards.shtml

Foundation for Critical Thinking. (June 1996). Valuable Intellectual Virtues. Retrieved from The Critical Thinking Community Web site: http://www.criticalthinking.org/resources/articles/valuable-intellectual-traits.shtml

Foundation for Critical Thinking. (2004). A Brief History of the Idea of Critical Thinking. Retrieved July 18, 2006, from The Critical Thinking Community Web site: http://www.criticalthinking.org/aboutCT/briefHistoryCT.shtml

Halfman, P. (2001). *100% language: Activities for language comprehension—primary and intermediate.* East Moline, IL: LinguiSystems, Inc.

Harlow, R., & Morgan, G. (1991). *175 amazing nature experiments.* New York: Random House.

Huisingh, C., & Huisingh, R. (2003). *Science trek: A reading comprehension game.* East Moline, IL: LinguiSystems, Inc.

Huisingh, R., Bowers, L., Johnson, P., LoGiudice, C., & Orman, J. (2003). *Story comprehension to go.* East Moline, IL: LinguiSystems, Inc.

Parry, T., & Gregory, G. (1998). *Designing brain-compatible learning.* Arlington Heights, IL: SkyLight Professional Development.

Paul, R.W., Binker, A.J.A., & Weil, D. (1995). *Critical thinking handbook: K-3rd grades.* Dillon Beach, CA: Foundation for Critical Thinking.

Paul, R.W., Binker, A.J.A., Martin, D., Vetrano, C. & Kreklau, H. (1995). *Critical thinking handbook: 6-9th grades.* Dillon Beach, CA: Foundation for Critical Thinking.

Piaget, J. (1977). *Studies in reflecting abstraction* (Robert L. Campbell, Ed. & Trans.). London: Psychology Press. (Original work published 1977)

Petreshene, S.S. (1994). *Brain teasers!* West Nyack, New York: The Center for Applied Research in Education.

Scriven, M., & Paul, R. (1996). Defining Critical Thinking: A Draft Statement for the National Council for Excellence in Critical Thinking. Retrieved from The Critical Thinking Community Web site: http://www.criticalthinking.org/page.cfm?PageID=410&CategoryID=51

Tagholm, S. (2001). *The complete book of the night: Wonder, workers and wildlife.* Kingfisher, NY: Houghton Mifflin Co.

31-14-98765